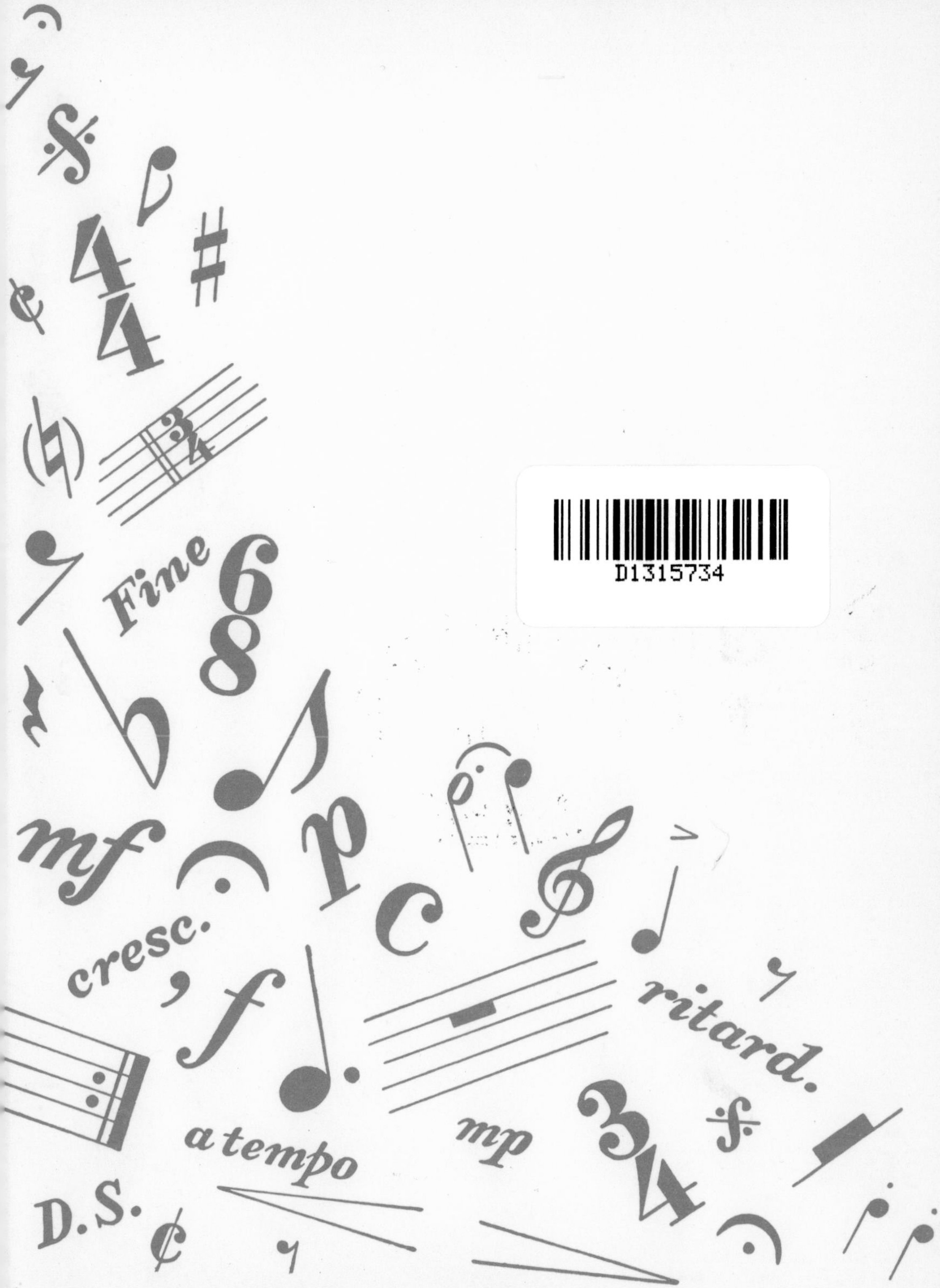
Fine
mf
p
cresc.
ritard.
a tempo
mp
D.S.

A SINGING SCHOOL

OUR LAND OF SONG

NEW EDITION

Editors:

Theresa Armitage
Peter W. Dykema
Gladys Pitcher
David Stevens
J. Lilian Vandevere

Advisory Editors:

Charles H. Farnsworth
Herman F. Smith

Art Editor:

Martha Powell Setchell

Summy-Birchard Publishing Company

Evanston • Illinois

Dear Boys and Girls:

Here is a book of songs which we hope you will enjoy — songs about our country and its great men, songs which Americans have sung for many years, songs written by living Americans, songs from our good neighbor countries to the north and south, and songs from other countries which have been the homes of many who are now Americans.

We know that you love America and are growing up to be her loyal citizens, — thankful for her gifts, honoring her history, interested in her welfare, and preparing to accept the responsibilities that will be yours as her citizens.

May this book help you to become fine Americans, with a love of singing and an understanding of music.

The Editors and Publishers

P. S. You know these songs have piano accompaniments in Our Land of Song, Book of Accompaniments.

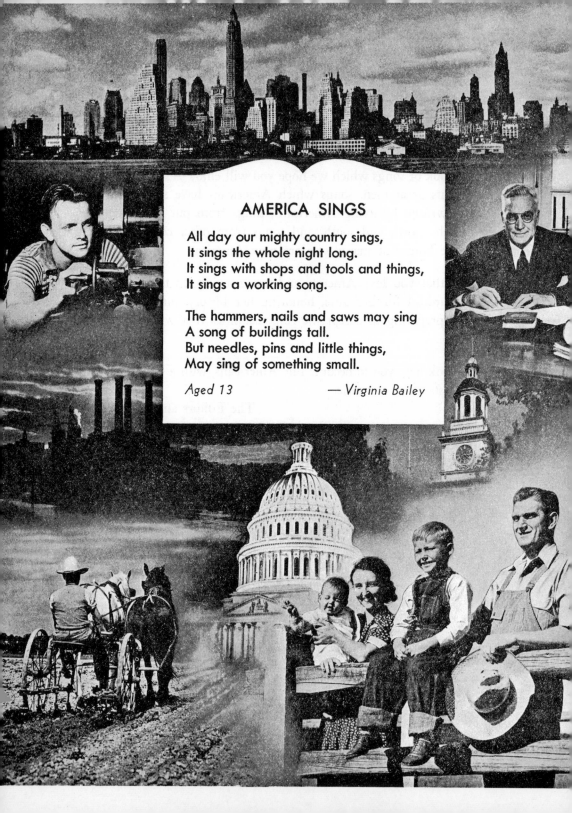

AMERICA SINGS

All day our mighty country sings,
It sings the whole night long.
It sings with shops and tools and things,
It sings a working song.

The hammers, nails and saws may sing
A song of buildings tall.
But needles, pins and little things,
May sing of something small.

Aged 13   — *Virginia Bailey*

The Music Road

"Let music swell the breeze. . ."

COVERED WAGON DAYS

*Composed by Fifth Grade Children
Pasadena (California) City Schools

1. A - cross the plains roll our wag - on trains, On the
2. We will camp to - night at a pleas - ant site And we'll

way to the gold fields far, Where the cat - tle prowl and the
sing to the ban - jo's strum; To the fid - dle's squeal we will

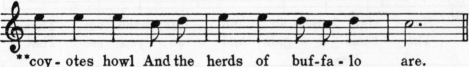

**coy - otes howl And the herds of buf - fa - lo   are.
dance a   reel And be   gay, what - ev - er may   come.

CHORUS

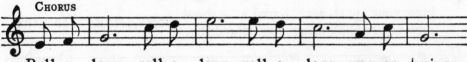

Roll a - long, roll a - long, roll a - long, wag - on trains.

Roll a - long, roll a - long, roll a - long, a - cross the plains.

*Teacher, Miss Ethel B. Tassey

**Pronounced "kī-ōtes"

5

COME, LET US TO THE BAGPIPE'S SOUND

Johann Sebastian Bach

Brightly

Come, let us to the bag - pipe's sound, The

mer - ry, mer - ry, mer - ry, mer - ry, mer - ry, mer - ry sound,

Tread out a meas-ure gay. 1.With right foot first and
2.Now hands a - cross and

left foot then, Turn right a - bout and back a - gain;
change your place, Then turn your part - ner face to face;

Now right hand in and left hand out, Then
The same a - gain, and so you see That

turn your part - ner round a - bout. Come, let us to the
now you're back where you should be.

bag - pipe's sound, The mer - ry, mer - ry, mer - ry, mer - ry,

mer - ry, mer - ry sound, Tread out a meas - ure gay.

This song is from the "Peasant Cantata" by Johann Sebastian Bach.

6

"Let's blend our voices. You sing 'mi-fa-mi' while I sing 'do-re-do.' Ready! —"

"I know! Let's all try it! We can divide into teams and sing different notes."

"We will be captains. Your side can sing 'do-ti-do,' while we sing 'mi-re-mi'!"

TUNEFUL TIM SAYS:

Have you ever sung two-part music? If you have, I know you thought it great fun, and liked to listen to the other part while you sang your own part.

You will find many such songs in this book as well as some jolly songs to sing in unison. Sometimes only part of the song will be in two parts, and sometimes the lower part, or "alto," will sing the tune, or "melody," as we call it.

See how nicely you can blend these two parts. Sing them slowly and smoothly. I just know that you will have more fun than ever with your singing.

MORNING HYMN

Jane Landon

Robert W. Gibb

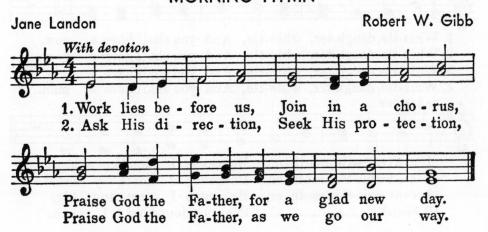

1. Work lies be-fore us, Join in a cho-rus,
2. Ask His di-rec-tion, Seek His pro-tec-tion,

Praise God the Fa-ther, for a glad new day.
Praise God the Fa-ther, as we go our way.

7

Sidney Rowe

Moravian Tune

1. Summer is o - ver, and now come Oc-to-ber days;
Old Mis-ter Frost has been set - ting the trees a-blaze. Painting the
2. Harvest is o - ver, the bar - ley and oats are stored; Thanksgiving's
Pumpkins are gath-er'd and heaped in a gold-en hoard.

green leaves all yel - low and red, In the for-est and wood-land ways.
on - ly a few weeks a - way, Sing hur-rah for the fes - tive board!

Have you heard, on the piano or on records, "Oc-tober" and "In Autumn," both by the American composer, Edward MacDowell? How do they compare with this song and the autumn songs on other pages?

WHISTLE, DAUGHTER, WHISTLE

Traditional

Early American Song

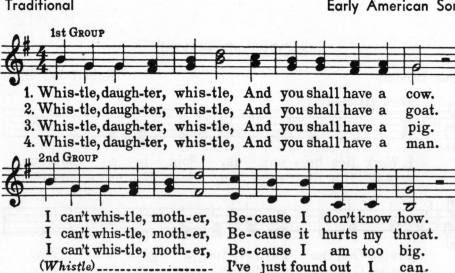

1st GROUP

1. Whis-tle, daugh-ter, whis-tle, And you shall have a cow.
2. Whis-tle, daugh-ter, whis-tle, And you shall have a goat.
3. Whis-tle, daugh-ter, whis-tle, And you shall have a pig.
4. Whis-tle, daugh-ter, whis-tle, And you shall have a man.

2nd GROUP

I can't whis-tle, moth-er, Be-cause I don't know how.
I can't whis-tle, moth-er, Be-cause it hurts my throat.
I can't whis-tle, moth-er, Be-cause I am too big.
(Whistle) - - - - - - - - - - - I've just found out I can.

8

THEY ALL MAKE MUSIC

Sidney Rowe   Betsy Adams

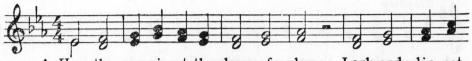

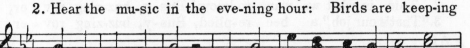

1. Hear the mu-sic at the dawn of day: Lark and lin-net
2. Hear the mu-sic in the eve-ning hour: Birds are keep-ing

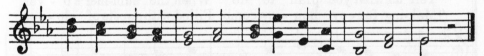

on their sky-ward way;   Bees are humming, and the par-tridge
in their leaf-y bow'r;   Soft winds sigh-ing, and the trees re -

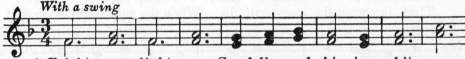

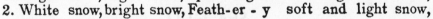

drumming, And they all make mu-sic at the dawn of day.
ply-ing, And they all make mu-sic in the eve-ning hour.

A WINTER SONG

Jane Landon   Robert W. Gibb

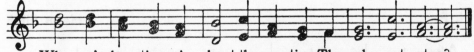

1. Bright snow, light snow, Spark-ling and shin-ing white snow,
2. White snow, bright snow, Feath-er-y soft and light snow,

When we're boasting A - bout the coasting, Then why not stay?
While we're say-ing, "Good snow for playing"; You melt a - way!

Can you sing and then whistle these phrases?

9

BEES IN WINTER

Sidney Rowe

Lowell Bond

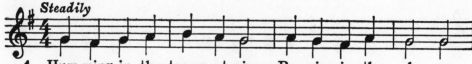

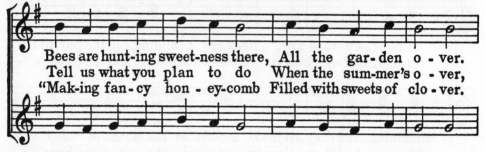

Steadily

1. Hum-ming in the trump-et vine, Buz-zing in the clo - ver,
2. This is what we want to know, Bus-y, buz-zing rov - er,
3. "That's our job," a bee re-plied, Bus-y, buz-zing rov - er,

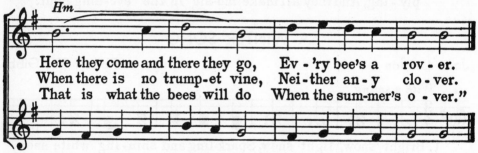

Bees are hunt-ing sweet-ness there, All the gar-den o - ver.
Tell us what you plan to do When the sum-mer's o - ver,
"Mak-ing fan-cy hon - ey-comb Filled with sweets of clo - ver.

Hm

Here they come and there they go, Ev - 'ry bee's a rov - er.
When there is no trump-et vine, Nei - ther an - y clo - ver.
That is what the bees will do When the sum-mer's o - ver."

SEA GULL

H. F.

Helen Fitch

1. Sea gull, sea gull, Mourn-ful-ly you cry.
2. Sea gull, sea gull, Take your si - lent way.

Sea gull, sea gull, Drift - ing slow-ly by.
Sea gull, sea gull, High a - bove the spray.

CLEVER CRICKET

Clinton Cole

Robert W. Gibb

A crick-et played a ti-ny note, Chirp! Chirp! Chirp! Chirp!

It seems he learned it all by rote, Chirp! Chirp! Chirp!

I asked him why he did not sing. Said he, "I'd rath-er

pluck a string. I use my head and save my throat—Chirp! Chirp! Chirp!"

Let's try this with various sounds, such as humming or cooing on the long notes, and "plucking a string" on the short, or "staccato," notes.

THE GARDENER'S SONG

Lewis Carroll   George Frederick McKay

Here is a song "just for fun!"

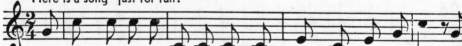

He thought he saw an el - e - phant That played up - on a fife; He
He thought he saw a rat-tle-snake That ques-tioned him in Greek; He
He thought he saw a kan-ga-roo That worked a cof-fee mill; He
He thought he saw an Al-ba-tross That flut-tered round the lamp; He

3 *

looked a-gain, and found it was a Let-ter from his wife.
looked a-gain, and found it was The Mid-dle of Next Week.
looked a-gain, and found it was A Veg-e-ta-ble Pill.
looked a-gain, and found it was A Pen-ny Post-age Stamp.

"At length I re - al - ize," he said, "The bit - ter-ness of life!" He
"The one thing I re - gret," he said, "Is that it can-not speak!" He
"Were I to swal-low this," he said, "I should be ver-y ill!" He
"You'd best be get-ting home," he said "The nights are ver-y damp." He

thought he saw a buf - fa - lo Up - on the chim-ney piece. He
thought he saw a Bank-er's Clerk De-scend-ing from a bus; He
thought he saw a Coach and Four That stood be-side his bed; He
thought he saw a Gar-den Door That o - pened with a key; He

*This sign shows that the pianist plays
three measures here. Those who play in
a school orchestra may know this sign.

12

looked a-gain and found it was his sis-ter's hus-band's niece."Un-
looked a-gain and found it was A Hip-po-pot-a-mus. "If
looked a-gain and found it was A Bear with-out a Head."Poor
looked a-gain and found it was A Dou-ble-Rule-of-Three."And

less you leave this house,"he said,"I'll call for the po-lice!"
this should stay to dine," he said,"There won't be much for us!"
thing;" he said,"Poor sil-ly thing, It's wait-ing to be fed!"
all its mys-ter-y," he said,"Is clear as day to me!"

HOW FOOLISH!

Agnes Ainsley   William Peters

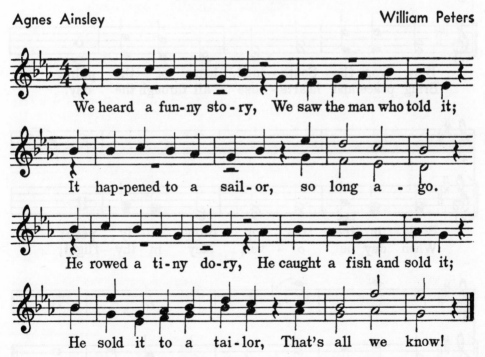

We heard a fun-ny sto-ry, We saw the man who told it;

It hap-pened to a sail-or, so long a-go.

He rowed a ti-ny do-ry, He caught a fish and sold it;

He sold it to a tai-lor, That's all we know!

Can you find the rhythm in the picture on the opposite page?
You will find a few other such rhythm pictures scattered
through the book. Perhaps you will enjoy looking for them.

THE SOUTH WIND

Sidney Rowe

Peter W. Dykema

Violin or flute obbligato

In moderate time

1. Blow, blow, thou soft wind, fra - grant with balm;
2. Blow thou at sun - rise, drive gloom a - way;

Blow from the South - land, home of the palm.
Bring peace and hearts - ease all through the day.

Birds in the tree - top drow - si - ly peep;
When day is o - ver, stay in thy flight;

Blow, blow, thou South Wind, rock them to sleep.
Guard us in slum - ber, all through the night.

A MARKET SONG

Adapted from the original   Czech Tune

Ah! (or a violin)

1. { I went to mar-ket with corn-meal, corn-meal,
   { Mice gnawed a hole in my corn-bag, corn-bag,
2. { Pi-geons ate all of my corn-meal, corn-meal,
   { Next year I'll keep all my har-vest, har-vest,

Ah!

Yel-low as gold was my corn-meal, corn-meal.
Out poured the meal from my corn-bag, corn-bag.
Now I've no mon-ey nor corn-meal, corn-meal.
So I can live on my har-vest, har-vest.

SI, SEÑOR

Mary de Haven   Argentine Tune

Gaily (Girls hum alto on 1st verse, boys on 2nd verse)

(He) 1. I'll be a gay ca-bal-le-ro, And own a
(She) 2. I shall do Ar-gen-tine danc-es, And bend and
(Both) 3. Trips to the coun-try we men-tion Are far too

ranch; I'll be a hand-some va-que-ro In
sway, Send-ing the se-ñors bright glanc-es, But
long, So we give up our in-ten-tion. In-

far Ar-gen-ti-na, if I have a chance.
then, Ar-gen-ti-na is too far a-way!
stead we are sing-ing this Ar-gen-tine song.

GOD REST OUR GLORIOUS LAND

Oliver Wendell Holmes (adapted)
2nd verse by David Stevens

Carl Engel

In solemn measure

1. God rest our glo-rious land Safe in Thy might-y hand
2. Lord, let Thy lov-ing care Guard all our na-tion fair;
3. Lord, let war's tem-pest cease, Fold all the world in peace,

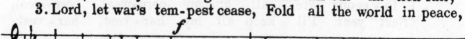

For-ev-er-more. Be Thou our guide and friend, Help us our
Guide us a-right. Lead us in Wis-dom's way, Lest from its
Un-der Thy wings! Make all the na-tions one, All hearts be-

homes de-fend; Let nev-er foe de-scend Up-on our shore.
path we stray; Hum-bly, with faith we pray For Thy pure light.
neath the sun, Till Thou shalt reign a-lone, Great King of Kings!

BE STILL!

Isaiah

Lilian Drake

Be still, and know that I am God.

Be still, and know that I am God.

16

ALL THROUGH THE NIGHT.

Harold Boulton

David Owen
Arranged by G. P.

1. Sleep, my child, and peace at-tend thee All through the night;
2. While the moon her watch is keep-ing All through the night;

Guard-ian an-gels God will send thee, All through the night.
While the wea-ry world is sleep-ing All through the night.

This descant may be sung or played upon an instrument.

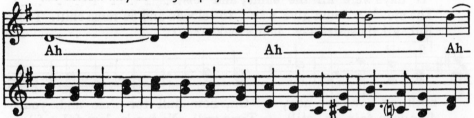

Ah_____ Ah_____ Ah__

Soft the drow-sy hours are creep-ing, Hill and vale in slum-ber steep-ing,
O'er thy spir-it gen-tly steal-ing, Vi-sions of de-light re-veal-ing,

Ah_____

I my lov-ing vig-il keep-ing, All through the night.
Breathes a pure and ho-ly feel-ing, All through the night.

Can you make your own quiet words for this?

17

THE SILVER LINING

Stephen Fay

Avery Wynne

Briskly

1. If, all the year a-round, the sun was al-ways glow-ing,
— seas were al-ways calm, and on-ly soft winds blow-ing,
2. The rain must some-times fall to keep our gar-dens grow-ing,
— gen-tle breeze will change, and storm-y winds be blow-ing,

1.

If ne'er a rain-drop fell, and skies were al-ways blue; If
If days were all the same, and *(omit . . . .)*
The stead-y sun give way to clouds and au-tumn chill. The
But all those drear-y hours make *(omit . . . .)*

2.

noth-ing ev-er new, Oh, how dull for me and you!
fair days fair-er still. Time will Na-ture's law ful-fil,

If days were all the same, and noth-ing ev-er new.
And all those sun-less hours make fair days fair-er still.

FROM THANKFUL HEARTS

Jane Landon

French Tune

With devotion

Sing for the world so spa-cious, Sing for the skies a-bove.

Fine

Sing, for our God is gra-cious, Sing, for His name is Love.
D.S. Warm was the time of grow-ing, Sing, then, a song of praise.

18

D.S. al fine

Clear was the time of sow-ing, Ten - der the A-pril days;

YOU AND I

J. Lilian Vandevere   Robert W. Gibb

Quietly

1. I went up where the hill was lift - ing
2. I went up where the clouds were fly - ing

I went down where the boats were drift-ing. Then we met, in the
I went down where the gulls were cry - ing. Then we sang, com-ing

pleas-ant weath-er, Where the gulls float-ed by.
home to - geth - er, Sang this song, you and I.

19

WHERE, O WHERE IS OLD ELIJAH?

Traditional

Old American Song

Where, O where is old E-li-jah, Where, O where is old E-li-jah,

Where, O where is old E-li-jah? Way down in the pro-mised land.

2. He went up in a fiery chariot,
He went up in a fiery chariot,
He went up in a fiery chariot,
Way down in the promised land.

3. By and by we'll go and see him, *etc.*

4. Where, O where is poor old Daniel? *etc.*

5. He went in a den of lions, *etc.*

6. By and by we'll go and see him, *etc.*

PEEP!

Clinton Cole

German Tune

Jokingly

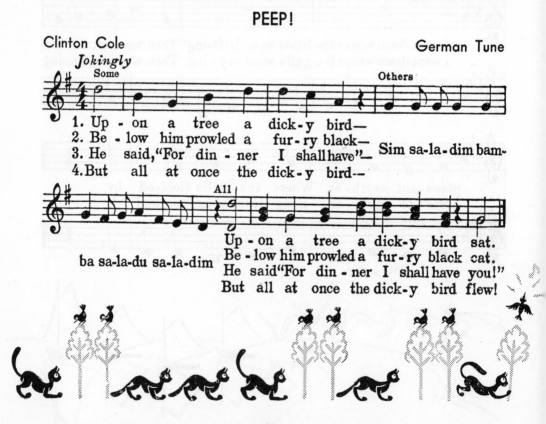

Some

1. Up - on a tree a dick-y bird—
2. Be - low him prowled a fur-ry black—
3. He said, "For din - ner I shall have"—
4. But all at once the dick-y bird--

Others

Sim sa-la-dim bam-

All

ba sa-la-du sa-la-dim

Up - on a tree a dick-y bird sat.
Be - low him prowled a fur-ry black cat.
He said "For din - ner I shall have you!"
But all at once the dick-y bird flew!

QUESTIONS

Foster B. Merriam   Lithuanian Tune

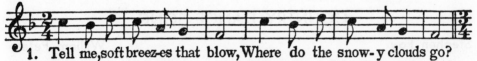

1. Tell me, soft breez-es that blow, Where do the snow-y clouds go?
2. Where do the for-est tunes start? Who teach-es thrush-es their art?

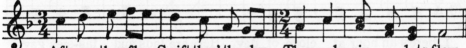

Aft-er they fly Swift thro' the sky, They make riv-u-lets flow.
God whispers words Soft to the birds, Then they learn them by heart.

FOLK DANCERS

Antonin Dvořák
(in *Slavic Dances*)

Is the musical feeling, or "color," of these chords different from
those you have sung before? Do you know how to name it?

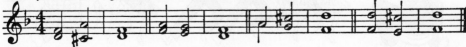

FOG

J. L. V.

Gladys Pitcher

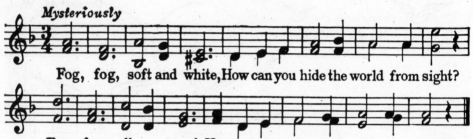

Fog, fog, soft and white, How can you hide the world from sight?

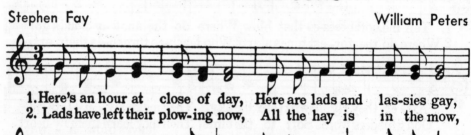

Fog, fog, all a-round, How can you creep, and make no sound?

COUNTRY DANCE SONG

Stephen Fay

William Peters

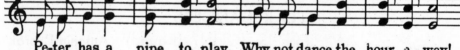

1. Here's an hour at close of day, Here are lads and las-sies gay,
2. Lads have left their plow-ing now, All the hay is in the mow,

Pe-ter has a pipe to play, Why not dance the hour a-way!
Ev-'ry lass has milked her cow, Time to have our danc-ing now.

What other dance tunes are found in this book? Here are the names of some country dance records: "Country Dance" from *Nell Gwynne Suite* by Edward German; "Eight Country Dances" by Mozart; "Shepherds Hey" by Percy Grainger; "Shepherd and Peasant" Dance by Edvard Grieg. If you have any of these, or others, you may like to share them with your schoolmates.

AUTUMN EVENING

Helen Fitch

Folk Tune
Descant H. W. L.

With motion

1. There's a tang to Oc - to-ber, and the ma-ples are gay.
2. By the hearth it is co-sy, with a fire burn-ing bright.

1. There's a tang, ma-ples are gay.
2. By the hearth, fire burn-ing bright.

But the oak trees are so-ber, rus-set leaves blow a - way.
Now the em-bers are ros-y, we'll have pop-corn to-night.

Oaks are brown, leaves blow a - way.
Em - bers glow, pop-corn to-night.

WHERE IS JOHN? (Round)

Abel Horne

Friedrich Smetana*

Where is John? The old white hen has left her pen, Oh, where is

John? The cows are in the corn a-gain, Oh, John!

*A noted Bohemian composer.

23

THE HERDSMAN
(According to the Poets)

Sidney Rowe   Swiss Tune

This descant may be sung, or played upon an instrument.

Ah_____

The herds-man leads a life of ease, Al-tho' he's up at dawn-ing,
And eats his fru-gal bread and cheese So ear-ly in the morn-ing.

Laughs, sings all the way, "U - li - u - li, u - li - ay!"

He drives his cat-tle on their way, And sings "U- li - lee - u - li - ay!"

Then to pass the time a - way, He sings "U - li - lee - ay!"

To pass time a - way, then, he sings "U - li - lee - ay!"

SING! (Round)

Traditional   Traditional

1
Sing when you're sor - row-ful, Sing when you're gay.

2
Sing at the rise of sun, Sing when the day is done,

24

Sing - ing is hap - pi - ness, Sing ev - 'ry - one!

2nd voice ends here

Sing - ing is hap - pi - ness, Sing ev - 'ry - one!

1st voice ends here

GO 'WAY, OLD MAN

Traditional

Southern Song

Quietly

1. Oh, I'll build me a lit-tle hut in the moun-tains so
2. Oh, I walk far a - way,— to for - get her I

high, For to gaze on my true love as she do pass by.
try, But I still seek the hill where I see her go by.

REFRAIN

Go 'way old man and leave me a - lone, For

I am a stran-ger and a long way from home.

25

OH, WHAT A LOT YOU'VE MISSED

Nonsense by Stephen Fay

Old American Tune

1. I had a dog, and a good dog, too, He'd rath-er eat than
2. I had a cow and her name was Maud, We worked a clev-er
3. I had a goat and a good goat, too, And ca-pers he would
4. I had a mule and a good mule, too, And how that mule could

not; He had a coat all spot-ted with spots, So we
scheme, We mixed her feed with piec-es of ice, And she
cut; He al-most rolled me o-ver one day, So I
go! We nev-er knew her fam-i-ly name, So we

al-ways called him Spot.
al-ways gave ice-cream.
called him Bill All-Butt; Sing low, sing high, I'll
al-ways called her "Whoa!"

tell you why, I shall put you on my list. If you

nev-er saw my won-der-ful { dog / cow / goat / mule } Oh, what a lot you've missed!

FEARLESS FISHERS

Clinton Cole

Gladys Pitcher

Not too fast

1. North, where the cold spray dash-es, Where the storm winds blow,
2. East, with a grey fog drift-ing, Where the dawn is pale,

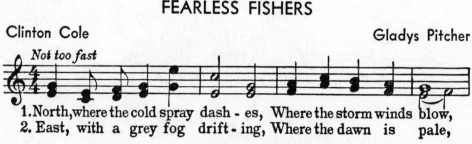

26

South, where the green wave dash-es— There our fish-ing boats go.
West, with the great peaks lift-ing, There our fish-ing boats sail.

COME AND SING!

J. L.   Jane Landon

Come and sing a song,   Ring-a-ding a-
Come,   a   song that's mer-ry, Ring - ding -
dong.
dong-down-der-ry. Songs al-ways end well When voic-es
Songs like this are fun,   Now we're done.
blend well. Songs   like   this are fun, But now we're done.

FOR A RAINY DAY

J. Lilian Vandevere

William Peters

Dull dark rain clouds hang, low and

Drip, drop, drip, drop, drip, drop, drip, drop, drip, drop, drip, drop,

grey. Day's pale light will

clouds are grey. Drip, drop, drip, drop, drip, drop, drip, drop,

fade and wane. Then read and

Day's pale light will fade and wane, To drip, drop, drip, drop,

dream this dull drear-y day. Read by the

drip, drop, drip, drop, Read this dull and drear-y day. Drip, drip, drop,

1.

fire to the plash of the au-tumn rain.

2.

rain.

Drip, drip, drop, Drip, drip, drop, au-tumn rain.

au-tumn rain.

THE FIRST STAR

Paul Hastings

Ignace Jan Paderewski
(in *Melodie*)

Smoothly

1. Star-light, sil-ver bright, And the first star I've seen to-night, O
send me, as I lie a-sleep, A lit-tle dream to have and keep,
have and keep. Bright star, sil-ver star, Tho' the vi-sions you
send a-far Will fade when we are wak-ing, Let mine come true!

2. Star-light, sil-ver bright, And the first star I've seen to-night, Up-
on me will you kind-ly beam And let me have my lit-tle dream,
lit-tle dream. Bright ray, sil-ver ray, Tho' I know you are
far a-way, I'll love you ev-'ry eve-ning, Make my wish true!

rall.   *a tempo*   *rall.*

YOUNG AMERICA SINGS

Clinton Cole

Stuart Bliss Hoppin

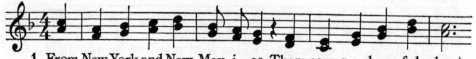

1. From New York and New Mex-i-co There comes a cheer-ful shout.
2. From Tex-as up to Or-e-gon The tune is loud and clear,

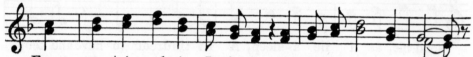

From moun-tain peaks in I-da-ho A stir-ring song rings out.—
Through Maine that song is roll-ing on, For ev-'ry-one to hear—

From Del-a-ware and Mich-i-gan You hear glad voic-es say,
From state to state that mu-sic ran, And we join in to-day.

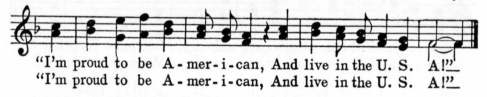

"I'm proud to be A-mer-i-can, And live in the U. S. A!"
"I'm proud to be A-mer-i-can, And live in the U. S. A!"

This tune was written by Franz Peter Schubert in his Fifth Symphony.
Can you write some words for it?

What other tunes or songs by Schubert do you know? It might be
nice to give a Schubert program, using songs you know and records
such as his "Moment Musicale No. 3" and his "Unfinished Symphony."

TUNEFUL TIM SAYS: Have you read the verses at the front of the book, called "America Sings"? They were written by a thirteen year old girl who loves America. Can you write a tune for them that is as lovely as the verses? It would be fun if you could make your music to sing in two parts.

"Virginia was thirteen and we are only ten, but I bet we can write a tune!"

"We will have to make it a very pretty song, because it is about America."

"This is fun, singing in two parts. Let's write another song!"

TWO-PART TRYOUT

Helen Fitch   Harvey Worthington Loomis

1. We can sing a song, we two, Such an eas-y thing to do. Two-part songs are charm-ing, Real-ly not a-larm-ing, An-y one can see it's true.

2. Such a dain-ty can-zo-net, Mel-o-dy you'll not for-get. We must phrase it neat-ly, Blend our voic-es sweet-ly, When we sing a gay du-et.

TUNEFUL TIM SAYS: Of course you remember the old jingle:

> "Humpty Dumpty sat on a wall,
> Humpty Dumpty had a great fall . . ."

Have you ever sung any songs in this tripping rhythm, which we mark $\frac{6}{8}\binom{2}{J.}$?

Here are some patterns that are often used in this rhythm:

Try tapping them over and over. Then let one group tap ♩. ♩. etc., while another taps ♩ ♪♩ ♪ etc., or ♪♪♪ ♪♪♪ etc.

Now tap any line of Humpty Dumpty, such as:

Hump-ty Dump-ty sat on a wall

Can you write the notes for it?

Now it will be easy to tap the rhythm of this song and then sing it.

OFF SHE GOES

Stephen Fay

Irish Jig Tune

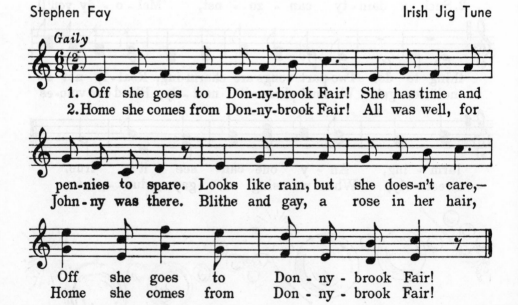

1. Off she goes to Don-ny-brook Fair! She has time and
2. Home she comes from Don-ny-brook Fair! All was well, for

pen-nies to spare. Looks like rain, but she does-n't care,—
John-ny was there. Blithe and gay, a rose in her hair,

Off she goes to Don-ny-brook Fair!
Home she comes from Don-ny-brook Fair!

A PICNIC MENU

Mary de Haven   Barbara Wentworth

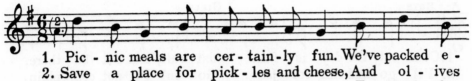

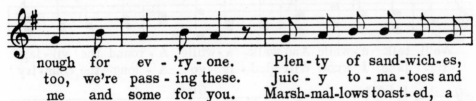

1. Pic - nic meals are cer - tain-ly fun. We've packed e -
2. Save a place for pick - les and cheese, And ol - ives
3. Fruit, of course, po - ta - to chips, too, E - nough for

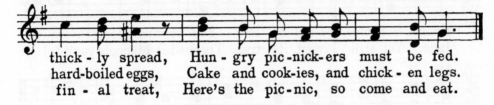

nough for ev - 'ry - one. Plen - ty of sand-wich-es,
too, we're pass - ing these. Juic - y to - ma-toes and
me and some for you. Marsh-mal-lows toast-ed, a

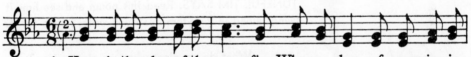

thick - ly spread, Hun - gry pic -nick-ers must be fed.
hard-boiled eggs, Cake and cook-ies, and chick - en legs.
fin - al treat, Here's the pic - nic, so come and eat.

TWILIGHT AT CAMP

Jane Landon   Lombardian Tune

1. Here in the glow of the camp-fire, When a day of camp-ing is
2. Warm is the glow of the em - bers, When the sum-mer dusk has de-

end - ed. Ris - es a qui - et ev - 'ning song.
scend - ed. Warm- er the light of friend - ly eyes,

1.
Voic-es are sweet-ly blend-ed.
2.
Seen as the camp-fire dies.

33

DIALOGUE

Helen Fitch

Scottish Tune

Gaily

BOYS GIRLS

1. Come out, the day is fair. Just wait, and I'll be there.
2. I'll go and call for Jane. Go on! I'll not com-plain.

ALL

We'll talk a-while And walk a-while A-round the vil-lage
But Jane I know Will glad-ly go A-long the coun-try

BOYS GIRLS

square. But come or we'll be late. You won't have long to wait.
lane. Yet still I wait, it's true. That's what I thought you'd do!

ALL

Why fuss and fret? It's ear-ly yet, The clock is strik-ing eight.
No need to fret, It's ear-ly yet! I'd rath-er walk with you.

TUNEFUL TIM SAYS: Read this poem and see how it swings along in $\frac{6}{8}$ rhythm. Can you write a tune for it?

What do we plant when we plant a tree?
We plant the ship which will cross the sea.
We plant the mast to carry the sails;
We plant the planks to withstand the gales—
The keel, the keelson, the beam, the knee;
We plant the ship when we plant the tree.

— *Henry Abbey*

WHEN MICHAEL PLAYS

J. Lilian Vandevere

Galway Tune

1. When you're hear-ing the lilt of a rol-lick-ing reel, A
2. 'Tis your-self will be caught by the charm of the sound, You'll

tune that is rip-pling with laugh-ter,— The Top of the
find you are foot-ing it glad-ly. The pra-ties are

Morn-ing, or Kit-ty O'-Neil— That feet will be fol-low-ing
like to jump out of the ground, And fol-low the fid-dle tune

aft-er. Then up gets Ter-rence with No-rah or Nell, To
mad-ly. You hum or whis-tle wher-ev-er you go The

dance with-out ev-er de-lay-ing. The mer-ry old mu-sic is
tune that your feet are o-bey-ing. A lep-re-chaun rides on the

cast-ing a spell, When Mi-chael the fid-dler is play-ing.
tip of his bow, When Mi-chael the fid-dler is play-ing.

Try dancing a Virginia reel to this tune and see how
nicely it goes, even though it is an Irish jig tune.

TRANCADILLO

Caroline Gilman

Francis H. Brown

With a swing

1. Will you come, maid-ens come, o'er the roll - ing blue wave, For the
2. Wake the cho - rus and song, and our oars shall keep time, While our

REFRAIN

love - ly should still be the care of the brave. Tran - ca -
hearts gen - tly beat to the mu - si - cal chime. Tran - ca -

dil - lo, tran - ca - dil - lo, Tran - ca - dil - lo - dil - lo - dil - lo -

dil - lo, With moon-light and star-light, we'll bound o'er the bil - low.

THE MANDARIN

David Stevens

Chinese Tune

1. Oh, see now he comes, The
2. Lo! now he is gone, The

Man - da - rin, with proud ma - jes - tic tread.
sun a - bove is shin - ing just the same.

36

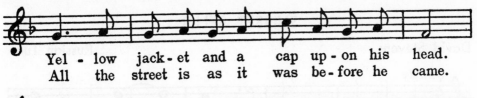

Yel - low jack - et and a cap up - on his head.
All the street is as it was be - fore he came.

Lo! now he comes! Ob - serve his state - ly air and haught - y stride!
Men come and go, And when they're gone we look an - oth - er way.

Lo! now he comes! let all the com - mon peo - ple stand a - side!
Lo! he is gone! But there will come an - oth - er one to - day.

RIGADOON

Mary de Haven   Henry Purcell

Briskly

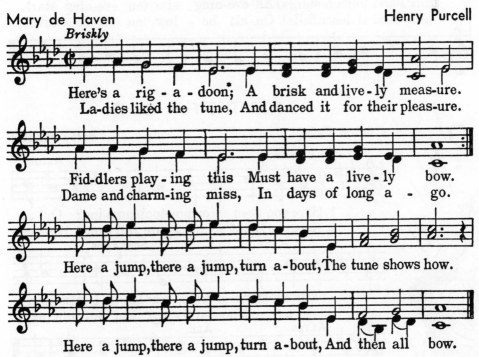

Here's a rig - a - doon; A brisk and live - ly meas - ure.
La - dies liked the tune, And danced it for their pleas - ure.

Fid - dlers play - ing this Must have a live - ly bow.
Dame and charm - ing miss, In days of long a - go.

Here a jump, there a jump, turn a - bout, The tune shows how.

Here a jump, there a jump, turn a - bout, And then all bow.

*A lively dance tune which probably came from France, though popular in England. There is a fine record of a "Suite of Four Pieces" by Purcell, that you may like to hear.

SUNSET BELLS

David Stevens   Russian Tune

1. The day is gone, so bright, so fair,____ With all its
2. The sun-set bells are heard a - far,____ And lo! there
3. The day is gone, the shad - ows grow,____ And si - lence

joy (with all its joy), With all its care (with all its care).
shines (and lo! there shines) An eve-ning star (an eve-ning star).
falls (and si-lence falls) On all be - low (on all be - low).

FOR THE FUN OF IT

Clinton Cole   Betsy Adams

SOPRANOS   ALTOS

1. Have you seen a camp-stool camp-ing? Or an
2. Have you heard a toll - gate toll - ing? Have you

SOPRANOS

old tramp steam-er tramp-ing? Though I blun-der,
seen a roll-book roll - ing? I'm in-quir-ing,

ALTOS   ALL

Still I won-der, Have you seen a draw-bridge draw?
Though I'm tir - ing, Have you seen a see - saw saw?

O SOLDIER, SOLDIER

Traditional   **Old English Song**

SHE

"O sol-dier, sol-dier, won't you mar-ry me, With your

HE

mus-ket, fife and drum?" "O no, sweet maid, I

Fine

can-not mar-ry thee, For I

have no coat to put on."
have no hat to put on."
have no gloves to put on."
have a wife of my own."

Then up she went to her grand-fa-ther's chest,
ver - y best,

And got him a hat of the ver - y, ver - y best,
coat
pair

She got him a hat of the ver - y, ver - y best,
coat
pair

D.C. al Fine

And the sol-dier put it on.
it
them

THE SIDE SHOW

David Stevens

1. Come, gents and la-dies, las-sies and lads, Broth-ers and
2. The dog-faced boy who grum-bles and growls, When the moon's

sis-ters, moth-ers and dads. Come walk right up with your nick-les
full he hol-lers and howls, The tat-tooed man, he's a won-der

and your dimes, I would let you in for noth-ing but we're
to be-hold, And a par-rot that is said to be a

hav-ing hard times. Right in-side there's a Can-ni-bal King, A
thou-sand years old. Next we come to the Skel-e-ton Man, The

Chi-nese gi-ant and his giv-en name is
Beard-ed La-dy, buy her pho-to if you

Ching. A Jer-sey calf with a
can. Per-form-ing seals and the

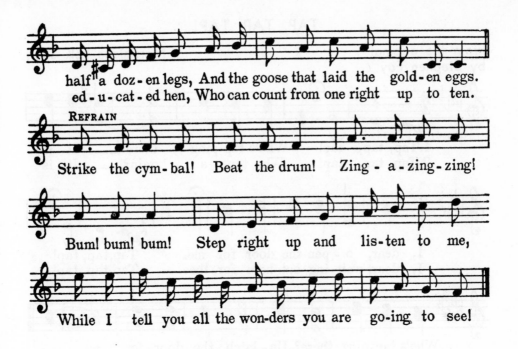

half a doz-en legs, And the goose that laid the gold-en eggs.
ed-u-cat-ed hen, Who can count from one right up to ten.

REFRAIN

Strike the cym-bal! Beat the drum! Zing-a-zing-zing!

Bum! bum! bum! Step right up and lis-ten to me,

While I tell you all the won-ders you are go-ing to see!

KEEP CLIMBING!

Jane Landon

Jane Landon
Descant by G. P.

This descant may be sung or played on a violin.

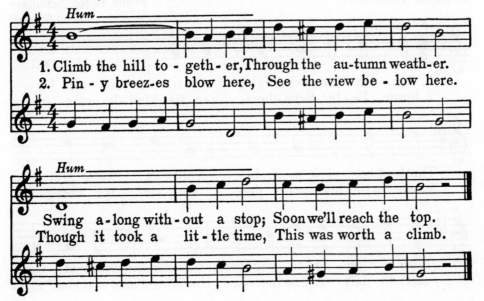

Hum

1. Climb the hill to-geth-er, Through the au-tumn weath-er.
2. Pin-y breez-es blow here, See the view be-low here.

Hum

Swing a-long with-out a stop; Soon we'll reach the top.
Though it took a lit-tle time, This was worth a climb.

TAP, TAP, TAP!

From the original
by Stephen Fay

Martinique Folk Song

(Melody)

1. Tap, tap, tap! Who's tap-ping there?____ It is
2. Tap, tap, tap! Who taps a - gain?____ It is

I, dear, o - pen the door for me. Tap, tap, tap!
I, dear, wait-ing out here for thee. Tap, tap, tap!

Who's tap-ping there? Un-latch the door for me.____
Who taps a - gain? 'Tis I, un-latch the door.____

FROM SCHUBERT'S PEN

J. Lilian Vandevere

Franz Peter Schubert
(in the *A Minor String Quartet*)

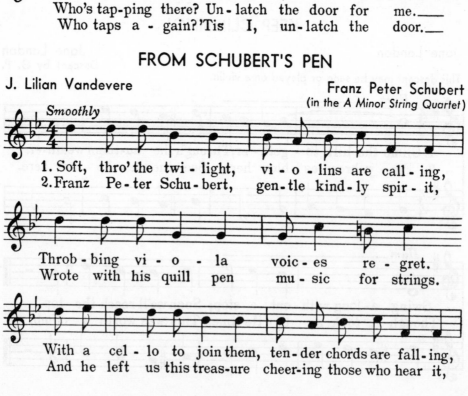

Smoothly

1. Soft, thro' the twi - light, vi - o - lins are call - ing,
2. Franz Pe - ter Schu - bert, gen - tle kind - ly spir - it,

Throb - bing vi - o - la voic - es re - gret.
Wrote with his quill pen mu - sic for strings.

With a cel - lo to join them, ten - der chords are fall - ing,
And he left us this treas - ure cheer - ing those who hear it,

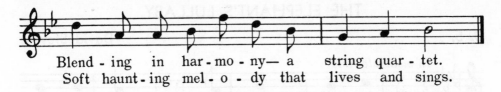

Blend - ing in har - mo - ny— a string quar - tet.
Soft haunt - ing mel - o - dy that lives and sings.

PASTORALE

Harvey Worthington Loomis

Swiss Folk Tune

Quietly

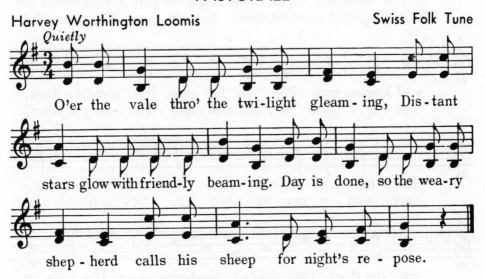

O'er the vale thro' the twi-light gleam - ing, Dis - tant
stars glow with friend-ly beam-ing. Day is done, so the wea-ry
shep - herd calls his sheep for night's re - pose.

COUNTER-MELODY

This counter-melody may be sung or played on an instrument.

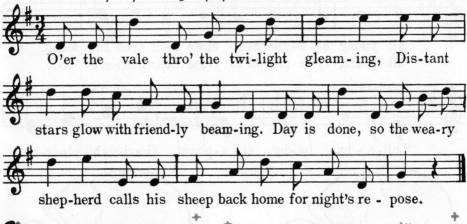

O'er the vale thro' the twi-light gleam - ing, Dis - tant
stars glow with friend-ly beam-ing. Day is done, so the wea-ry
shep-herd calls his sheep back home for night's re - pose.

THE ELEPHANT'S LULLABY

D. S.

David Stevens

In moderate time

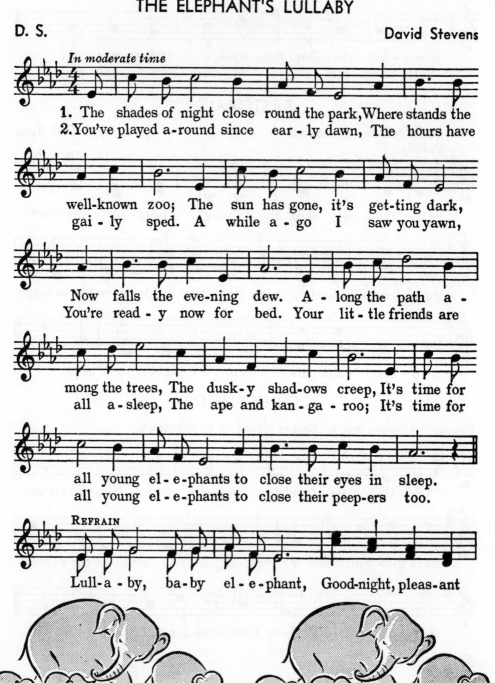

1. The shades of night close round the park, Where stands the
2. You've played a-round since ear-ly dawn, The hours have

well-known zoo; The sun has gone, it's get-ting dark,
gai-ly sped. A while a-go I saw you yawn,

Now falls the eve-ning dew. A-long the path a-
You're read-y now for bed. Your lit-tle friends are

mong the trees, The dusk-y shad-ows creep, It's time for
all a-sleep, The ape and kan-ga-roo; It's time for

all young el-e-phants to close their eyes in sleep.
all young el-e-phants to close their peep-ers too.

REFRAIN

Lull-a-by, ba-by el-e-phant, Good-night, pleas-ant

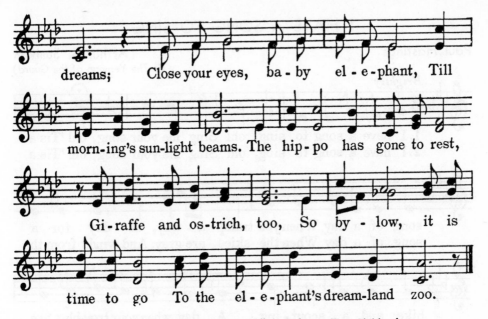

dreams; Close your eyes, ba-by el-e-phant, Till morn-ing's sun-light beams. The hip-po has gone to rest, Gi-raffe and os-trich, too, So by-low, it is time to go To the el-e-phant's dream-land zoo.

There is a record of "Jumbo's Lullaby" from *The Children's Corner* by Claude Debussy, that you might like to hear.

OLE AND CHRISTINE

M. Louise Baum

Danish Tune

In waltz time

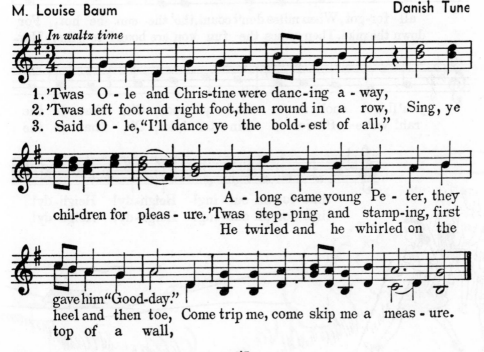

1. 'Twas O-le and Chris-tine were danc-ing a-way,
2. 'Twas left foot and right foot, then round in a row, Sing, ye
3. Said O-le, "I'll dance ye the bold-est of all,"

A-long came young Pe-ter, they
chil-dren for pleas-ure. 'Twas step-ping and stamp-ing, first
He twirled and he whirled on the

gave him "Good-day."
heel and then toe, Come trip me, come skip me a meas-ure.
top of a wall,

I HAVE A SONG TO SING

Paul Hastings

Arthur S. Sullivan
(in The Yeoman of the Guard)

Brightly

1. I have a song to sing, oh! Sing me your song, oh! 'Tis a
2. I have a song to sing, oh! Sing me your song, oh! 'Tis a

song of a day When you tramp a - way, A day for a
song of a day When the skies are gray, And winds from the

hike and a scout - ing, A day when your trou-bles are
north come a - shout - ing, When bells ring a - ting - a - ling

all for-got, When miles don't count, tho' the sun be hot, For
down the pike, Then comes the fun you are bound to like, Hur-

you'll get cool in a shad - y spot, Oh, that is the
rah! we're off for a win - ter hike, Oh, that is the

time for an out - ing! Heigh-dy! Heigh-dy!
time for an out - ing! Heigh-dy! Heigh-dy!

Rid-dle-i - o! Rid-dle-i - um! It's ho! my friends, for the
Rid-dle-i - o! Rid-dle-i - um! It's ho! my friends, for the

sum-mer's come, And that is the time for an out - ing.
win-ter's come, And that is the time for an out - ing.

DANCE, LITTLE SERAPHINA

Mary de Haven   Spanish Tune

Gaily

1. Dance, lit-tle Ser - a - phi - na, Dance with fly-ing feet,
2. Now from a lace man-til - la, Spar-kling eyes peep out,

Hark to the con-cer - ti - na, Play-ing in the street.
While in a se-gui-dil - la Danc-ers move a - bout,

Thro' the night you will hear a ser - e - nade, Sweet-ly sung,
As they play by the light of sil - ver stars, Cas-ta-nets,

light - ly played, With a gay lit - tle air and
gay gui-tars. And a - gain there is heard that

sweet re - frain, Far a - way in Spain.
mel - low strain, Far a - way in Spain.

47

JOIN IN!

Agnes Ainsley

Avery Wynne

With spirit

1. Give us a song to make us strong For all the work be-
2. Give us a song for sun-ny days And one for storm-y

fore us; Give us a song to set the pace And
weath-er; Give us a song that says "Chin up! We'll

join the rous-ing cho-rus. Sing! this is the time to start;
march a-long to-geth-er!" Sing! Ev-'ry-one likes a song;

Sing! Tak-ing a joy-ful part; Sing! Out of a
Sing! Car-ry the tune a-long; Sing! Mak-ing it

hap-py heart, Lift up your voice and sing!___
clear and strong, Lift up your voice and sing!___

It is told that a famous American designer of books receives many of his ideas for abstract designs from music patterns. Can you find the music pattern in the abstract designs on these two pages?

WHY NOT WHISTLE?

Clinton Cole

French Tune

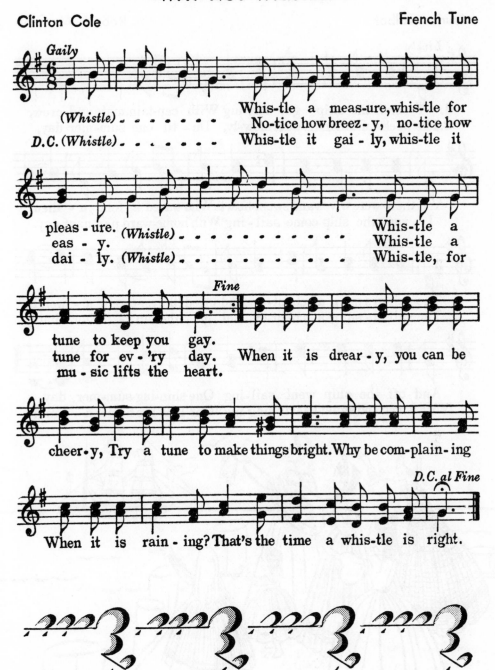

Gaily

(Whistle) . . . .
D.C. (Whistle) . . . .

Whis-tle a meas-ure, whis-tle for
No-tice how breez-y, no-tice how
Whis-tle it gai-ly, whis-tle it

pleas-ure. (Whistle) . . . .
eas-y. (Whistle) . . . .
dai-ly. (Whistle) . . . .

Whis-tle a
Whis-tle a
Whis-tle, for

Fine

tune to keep you gay.
tune for ev-'ry day. When it is drear-y, you can be
mu-sic lifts the heart.

cheer-y, Try a tune to make things bright. Why be com-plain-ing

D.C. al Fine

When it is rain-ing? That's the time a whis-tle is right.

I SAW THE SHIP GO SAILING

Maurice Talbot

Robert W. Gibb

1. I saw the ship go sail-ing With cap-tain, mate and crew,
2. The weeks and months went slow-ly, Un-til one sum-mer day,

And there were wives and sweet-hearts Who waved a fond a - dieu.
I saw the ship come sail - ing With home-ward pen-nant gay.

The sail-ors sang a chant-ey, And cried "the an-chor's a - weigh!"
The sail-ors sang a chant-ey, Let go the an - chor chain,

And off the ship went sail-ing One shin-ing sum-mer day.
With wives and sweet-hearts sing-ing "Our lads are home a - gain!"

WHO WILL COME OUT?

Sidney Rowe

Victor Pierpont

With a marching swing

1. Who will come out and tramp to - day O - ver the
2. Who will come out and tramp with me? No one can

hills and far a - way? Tramp-ing to - geth - er o - ver the
tell what we may see: But - ter-flies wing - ing, Rob-ins a -

heath - er, Sing - ing a mer - ry roun - de - lay.
sing - ing, May - be a bus - y hon - ey - bee.

OUT AND BACK

Mary de Haven

Harvey Worthington Loomis

With motion, not too fast

1. The waves go out to sea, They find a for - eign shore.
2. We may go far from home, See oth - er lands and men.

The waves go out to sea, And then come back once more.
We may go far from home, And then come back a - gain.

TRY A CONTRA DANCE

J. Lilian Vandevere   Peter W. Dykema

Moderately fast
Violin or Clarinet

1. Who could be dull or down-heart-ed— Fid-dlers play!
2. Mind what the call-er is say-ing, Don't be slow.

Hur-ry! the sets have been start-ed. Let's be gay.
Sim-ply keep time to the play-ing— Do-si-do.*

Down the center and back to place, Then cast off with an eas-y grace.
Now head couple goes down out-side, Up to place with an eas-y glide.

La-dies chain, ver-y plain, All may com-pre-hend it.
Tho' it's fun, now it's done. Prom-e-nade and. . . . end it.
For-ward then, back a-gain, Swing the one be-low you.
You would learn ev-'ry turn. Come, and we will. . . . show you.

*Do-si-do is an old American dance "call."

MORRIS DANCE
(May Day Dance)

David Stevens

Old English Morris Dance

Gaily

ALL

Strike up a meas-ure spright-ly and gay, And we'll
Dance in the gar-den, dance on the lea To a

Fine BOYS

dance an i-dle hour a-way. Green-ly grow the rush-es,
Mor-ris mu-sic, light and free.

bud-ding is the wil-low, Spring now is here and all is fair,

GIRLS

And she rides on the south wind, sweet and warm with May,

ALL

And a wreath of haw-thorne decks her hair. Why not dance when
Say fare-well to

D. C. al Fine

gai-ly songs re-sound In the trees and hedg-es all a-round.
toil and work-a-day, For the dance will drive dull care a-way.

The morris dance is a step, hop, step, hop, etc. Can you dance it?

TUNEFUL TIM SAYS: Can you hear and *feel* the "long-short" notes all through
this song? What a jolly, tripping rhythm they give it! And doesn't this rhythm
make the song sound gay—as if someone really wanted to dance?

Can you tap the steady, quarter-note pulses while you sing the song, watching
the notes? Doesn't it seem natural to have the "long-short" notes both sung to
one pulse?

A RAILROAD RHYME

J. L. V.

J. Lilian Vandevere

Once there was a roll-ing, rum-bling train, train,
train, train On the rail-road, rail-road, rail-road, rail-road
Lack-a-wan-na, Lack-a-wan-na, Lack-a-wan-na, Lack-a-wan-na
Chat-ta-noo-ga, Chat-ta-noo-ga, Chat-ta-noo-ga, Chat-ta-noo-ga
line;____ And it went chu-ca-chu, chu-ca-
chu, chu-ca-chu, chu-ca-chu-ca-chu-ca-
chu-ca-chu, on the rail-road, rail-road, rail-road, rail-road,
chu-ca-chu-ca-chu, on the rail-road line.____

At the top of the next page are patterns and pictures showing how the "long-short" (♪. ♪) notes fit into one pulse. Can you say them, tap them, and sing them?

54

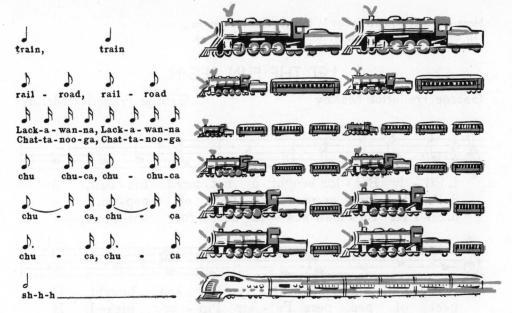

train,   train

rail - road, rail - road

Lack-a-wan-na, Lack-a-wan-na
Chat-ta-noo-ga, Chat-ta-noo-ga

chu   chu-ca, chu - chu-ca

chu -   ca, chu   ca

chu -   ca, chu - ca

sh-h-h _____

Be sure to make the quick notes short enough.

Here are the music names: ♩ = undivided pulse; ♪♪ = evenly divided pulse; ♪. ♪ = unevenly divided pulse.

Now let's turn back to page 32 and compare this jolly rhythm ²/₄(²/₄) ♪. ♪♪. ♪ with the one there ⁶/₈(²/₄) ♩ ♪♩ ♪. Can you understand and feel that the short note is shorter in ♪. ♪ than in ♩ ♪ ? Here is one way of comparing them:

Count one——— two———; one——— two———

This seems like an arithmetic lesson,—and of course there is a mathematical likeness. But a musical person must *feel* the difference. The best way to do this is to remember good musical examples, and remember to make the short note a little shorter in ♪. ♪ than in ♩ ♪ .

Even if you find the short note first,—like this: ♪♪. , it should be very easy for you to sing. Look at the song on page 125 (Wait, Old Mule). Say to yourselves, "name was Minnie," and you will have ♪ ♪ ♪♪. ; or, "cotton grows," and you will have ♪♪. ♩ .

Here are a few more songs in this rhythm for you to tap and sing. You will find others throughout the book.

LET THE FUN BEGIN

George Frederick McKay   George Frederick McKay

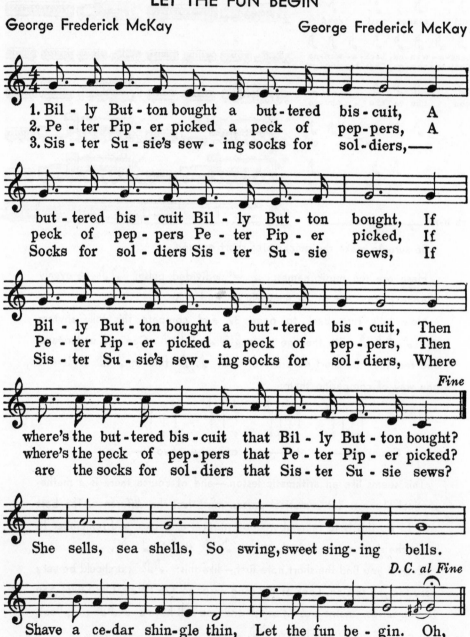

1. Bil - ly But - ton bought a but - tered bis - cuit, A
2. Pe - ter Pip - er picked a peck of pep - pers, A
3. Sis - ter Su - sie's sew - ing socks for sol - diers,——

but - tered bis - cuit Bil - ly But - ton bought, If
peck of pep - pers Pe - ter Pip - er picked, If
Socks for sol - diers Sis - ter Su - sie sews, If

Bil - ly But - ton bought a but - tered bis - cuit, Then
Pe - ter Pip - er picked a peck of pep - pers, Then
Sis - ter Su - sie's sew - ing socks for sol - diers, Where

Fine

where's the but - tered bis - cuit that Bil - ly But - ton bought?
where's the peck of pep - pers that Pe - ter Pip - er picked?
are the socks for sol - diers that Sis - ter Su - sie sews?

She sells, sea shells, So swing, sweet sing - ing bells.

D. C. al Fine

Shave a ce - dar shin - gle thin, Let the fun be - gin. Oh,

SONG OF CARCASSONNE

Translated by Henry Lee

Carcassonne Tune
(about 1500)

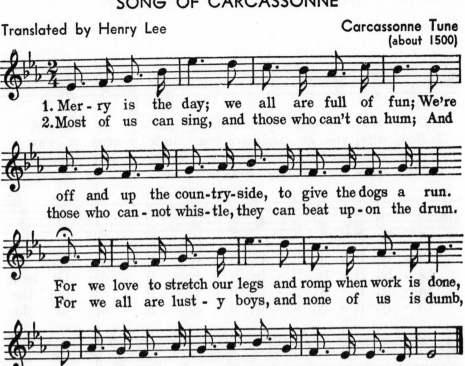

1. Mer-ry is the day; we all are full of fun; We're
2. Most of us can sing, and those who can't can hum; And

off and up the coun-try-side, to give the dogs a run.
those who can-not whis-tle, they can beat up-on the drum.

For we love to stretch our legs and romp when work is done,
For we all are lust-y boys, and none of us is dumb,

We are the lads of Lan-gue-doc, and rev-el in the sun.
We are the lads of Lan-gue-doc, you hear us when we come.

Carcassonne and Languedoc are two places in France.

REUBEN AND RACHEL (Canon)

American Folk Tune

When the first group has reached II, the second group starts at the beginning.

1. Reu-ben, Reu-ben, I've been think-ing, What a queer world this would be,
2. Ra-chel, Ra-chel, I've been think-ing, What a queer world this would be,

If the men were all trans-port-ed Far be-yond the north-ern sea.
If the girls were all trans-port-ed Far be-yond the north-ern sea.

57

THE COBBLER AND THE CROW

Revised by D. S.

Old American Song

1. There was a mer-ry cob-bler, bus-y as a bee,
2. Now, wife, you go and drive yon dusk-y crow a-way,
3. The cob-bler's wife she tried to drive a-way the crow,
4. Then spoke the mer-ry cob-bler at the close of day:

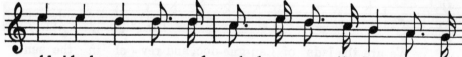

Li - ly, li - ly, li - ly, li - ly li - do; When an
Li - ly, li - ly, li - ly, li - ly li - do; Or he'll
Li - ly, li - ly, li - ly, li - ly li - do; But the
Li - ly, li - ly, li - ly, li - ly li - do; If the

old black crow came and perched up-on the tree,
perch and croak till the end-ing of the day, With his
more she tried, why the more he would-n't go,
crow won't go, we shall have to let him stay,

Qua! Qua! Qua! Qua! Li - ly, li - ly, li - ly, li - ly li - do.

DEFENDERS

J. Lilian Vandevere

Robert W. Gibb

1 View with e - la - tion Pride of the ña - tion, Brave men who de-
2. East where the dawns rise, West where the day dies, See our ships go
3. Rid - ing the sky - way, Far, track-less high-way, Air - men fly a -
4. Where trop - ic sun glows, Where i - cy wind blows, Brave marines are

fend us. Drilled to per-fec - tion, Trained as pro-tec - tion,
sail - ing. Where waves are rol - ling, Watch-ing, pa-trol-ling,
bove us. Planes tuned and read - y Hands firm and stead-y,
stand-ing. No foe af-frights them, Dan - ger de-lights them,

They march out for us then (to guard us). Cour - age will lead them
They sail out for us then (to guard us). Tell their de-vo - tion,
They fly out for us then (to guard us). Wings lift to bear them,
Sol - diers trained for the sea (to guard us). Quick men for land-ing,

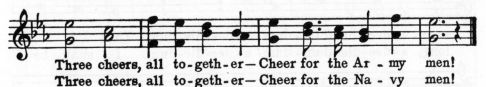

On where we need them, Sing their praise a - gain (We sing it!)
Pride of the o - cean, Sing their praise a - gain (We sing it!)
Brave, fear - less air - men, Sing their praise a - gain (We sing it!)
Strong men for stand-ing, Sing their praise a - gain (We sing it!)

Three cheers, all to-geth - er — Cheer for the Ar - my men!
Three cheers, all to-geth - er — Cheer for the Na - vy men!
Three cheers, all to-geth - er — Cheer for the Air Corps men!
Three cheers, all to-geth - er — Cheer the Ma-rine Corps men!

THAT TROUBLESOME TUNE

Clinton Cole

Gladys Pitcher

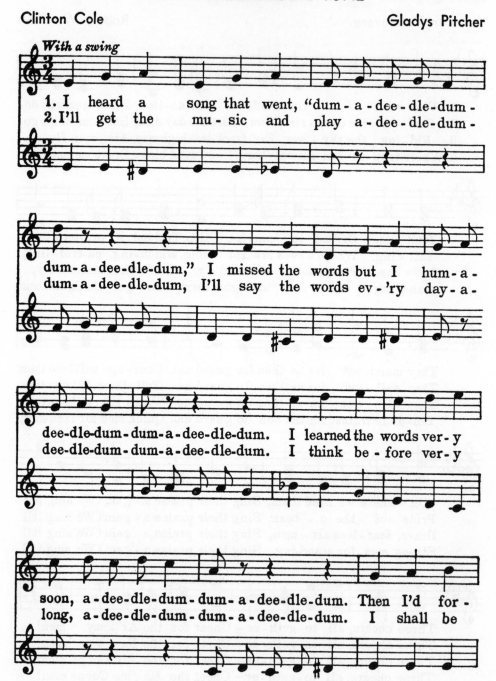

With a swing

1. I heard a song that went, "dum - a - dee - dle - dum -
2. I'll get the mu - sic and play a - dee - dle - dum -

dum - a - dee - dle - dum," I missed the words but I hum - a -
dum - a - dee - dle - dum, I'll say the words ev - 'ry day - a -

dee - dle - dum - dum - a - dee - dle - dum. I learned the words ver - y
dee - dle - dum - dum - a - dee - dle - dum. I think be - fore ver - y

soon, a - dee - dle - dum - dum - a - dee - dle - dum. Then I'd for -
long, a - dee - dle - dum - dum - a - dee - dle - dum. I shall be

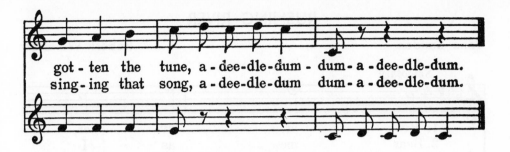

got - ten the tune, a - dee-dle-dum - dum - a - dee-dle-dum.
sing - ing that song, a - dee-dle-dum dum - a - dee-dle-dum.

LULLABY

Sidney Rowe

Basque Tune
Arranged by G. P.

This descant may be hummed or played on a violin.

Quietly

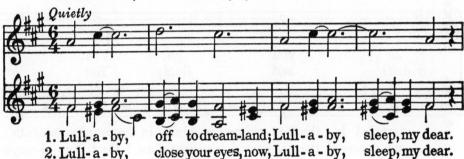

1. Lull - a - by, off to dream-land; Lull - a - by, sleep, my dear.
2. Lull - a - by, close your eyes, now, Lull - a - by, sleep, my dear.

Sail a - way where dreams are wait-ing, An - gels guard you, al - ways
All the lit - tle birds are sleep-ing, Sleep like them, and nev - er

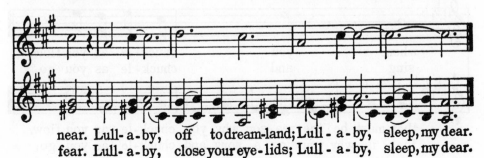

near. Lull - a - by, off to dream-land; Lull - a - by, sleep, my dear.
fear. Lull - a - by, close your eye - lids; Lull - a - by, sleep, my dear.

RUSHING RIVER

Jane Landon

Robert W. Gibb

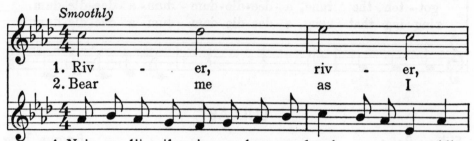

Smoothly

1. Riv - er, riv - er,
2. Bear me as I

1. Nois-y lit-tle riv-er, how you laugh as you run, All
2. O'er your rip-pling cur-rent I can drift in a boat, And

as you go, You
drift and float; You

dap-pled in the shad-ow and a-shine in the sun; You seem to
un-der-neath the wil-lows I can dream as I float; You al-ways

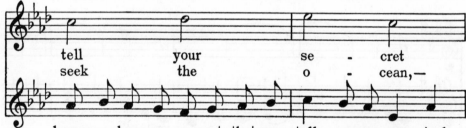

tell your se - cret
seek the o - cean,—

know a hap-py se-cret, that you tell as you go, And
think a-bout the o-cean, far a-way, as you flow, And

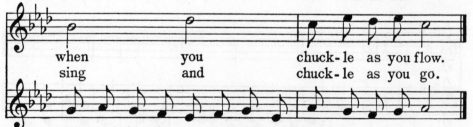

when you chuck-le as you flow.
sing and chuck-le as you go.

that must be the rea-son why you chuck-le as you flow.
that is why you sing a song, and chuck-le as you go.

RIO GRANDE

American Sailor's Chantey

Traditional

ONE VOICE ... ALL

1. O say, were you ev-er in Ri - o Grande? A - way___
2. Yon Liv-er-pool la-dies, we'd have you to know,

ONE VOICE

Ri - o!___ It's there that the riv-ers run down gold-en sand,
We're bound to the South and, come on, let us go,

ALL

And we're bound for the Ri-o Grande. And a - way___ to

Ri-o!___ Oh,___ you Ri-o! So fare you well, my

bon-nie young girl, For we're bound for the Ri-o Grande.

A TUNEFUL TALE

J. L. V.

J. Lilian Vandevere

All the exclamations, such as "Do tell!" may be spoken if you like.

1. I know a lit-tle man who had a wife — Do
2. Her un-cle was a wiz-ard on the drum — Yes
3. The lit-tle man di-rect-ed, so they say — One,

tell! He played a lit-tle tune up-on the fife — Well,
ma'am! He played it with a par-a-did-dle-dum — Flim-
two! And soon the fun-ny group knew how to play — That's

well! While she fol-lowed suit And played on the flute, With
flam. He played all the traps With rap-tap-i-taps, And
true. They played ev-'ry note That great mas-ters wrote, And

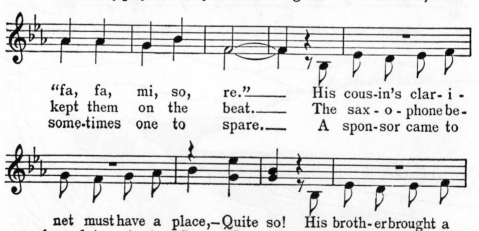

"fa, fa, mi, so, re."___ His cous-in's clar-i-
kept them on the beat.___ The sax-o-phone be-
some-times one to spare.___ A spon-sor came to

net must have a place,—Quite so! His broth-er brought a
longed to sis-ter Sue,— Hi - hi! And she could play in
hear them all re-hearse—One day, And said "I real-ly

lust - y dou - ble bass, Sing low! And when they'd be - gun,
ev - 'ry shade of blue, Oh, my! They played ev - 'ry score
think you might be worse!" Hey, hey! He soon had them sign

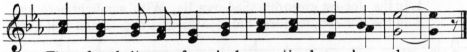

They found it was fun, And prac - ticed ev - 'ry day.___
Three times, may - be more, And then they'd say "Re - peat!"___
On each dot - ted line, And now they're on the air!___

FOR A PICNIC

Agnes Ainsley   French Tune

Come out and go a tramp-ing, come out and climb a hill,
___ not be back till ev-'ning, so bring a lunch a - long,
D.S. who'd re-fuse to join us, and who would stay in town?

Where far a - bove the crowd-ed streets the woods are green and
The trail will be an eas - y one, when tak - en with a
Come sit with us a - top a hill, and watch the sun go

still. We'll
. . . song. At lunch time we'll build a fire be-side a bub-bling
. . . down.

D. S. al Fine

brook, And oh, what an ap-pe-tite, when steak be-gins to cook! Then

65

THE FOREST GREEN

David Stevens

Louis Adolphe Coerne

Smoothly and quietly

1. In the for-est green dim shad-ows lie, With sun-light here and
2. In the for-est green are hid-den things, Un-seen and yet quite

there, And a qui - et breeze floats gen-tly by, To
near; On a leaf-y bough the lin-net sings A

cool the sum - mer air. There's a bus - y brook that
song we love to hear. When the eve-ning comes and

swift-ly flows, Its wa-ters pure and cold; On its mos-sy
all a-round The out-er world is still, From a - far there

bank A cow-slip grows Like a glimpse of fair - y gold.
comes the mourn-ful sound Of the lone - ly whip-poor- will.

CANOE SONG

David Stevens

Robert W. Gibb

With motion

1. Winds of morn-ing, blow kind-ly, blow gen-tly, Oh, skies be
2. Fear not, fish-es, there's noth-ing to fright-en, We mean no

clear and blue; Lake, be calm for to-
harm to you; Swans, be tran-quil, we

day we are go-ing to float our birch ca-noe.
ask on-ly pas-sage to float our birch ca-noe.

Up as far as the Fair-y Glen, Turn a-
Teal and mal-lard, you need not fly, Soon our

bout and come back a-gain, We'll dip our pad-dles and
bark will have passed you by, Soon our

sing a ca-noe song, Hal-lee, Hal-la, Hal-loo.

CHIT-CHAT

J. Lilian Vandevere   Peter W. Dykema

Busily

CHIT

1. "And how are you to-day?   I hope you're well. I've
2. "Just fan-cy meet-ing you,   and now I'll run. I

CHAT

1. "And how are you to-day, my dear? I hope you're well. I've
2. "Just fan-cy meet-ing you, my dear, and now I'll run. I

some-thing I must say,   so let me tell. I talked with
have so much to do,   that must be done. Ann But-ler

some-thing I must say, my dear, so let me tell.
have so much to do, my dear, that must be done.

Ma-ry Snow.   She lost her lat-est beau.
broke her arm.   Lem Tay-lor sold his farm.

But have you heard—   Why, that's ab-surd!
Oh, yes, I know—   You told me so.

68

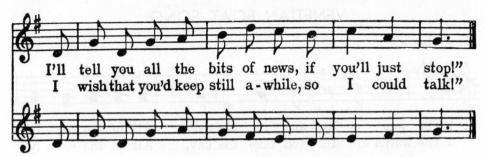

I'll tell you all the bits of news, if you'll just stop!"
I wish that you'd keep still a-while, so I could talk!"

You may sometime hear these records: "Good Morrow, Gossip
Joan," an English folk song, and "Gossips," by A. Dubensky.

A SERENADE TO NINA

J. L. V.

Tuscan Tune

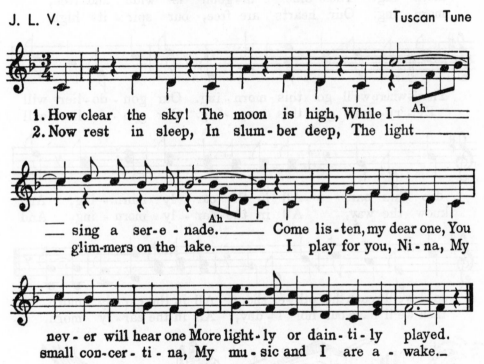

1. How clear the sky! The moon is high, While I Ah____
2. Now rest in sleep, In slum-ber deep, The light____

____ sing a ser-e-nade.____ Ah____ Come lis-ten, my dear one, You
____ glim-mers on the lake.____ I play for you, Ni-na, My

nev-er will hear one More light-ly or dain-ti-ly played.
small con-cer-ti-na, My mu-sic and I are a-wake.___

Who can tell how many eggs
Eggplants lay,—
How much milk a milkweed gives
Every day?

Can you make a tune for this, using dotted eighths and sixteenths?

VENETIAN BOAT SONG

Henry Snow

Italian Tune

1. The sun is up and so are we, All in the ear-ly morn-ing. The blue la-goon is wide and free, That's where we'll go this morn-ing. Our gon-do-lier will dip his oar, All in the ear-ly morn-ing, And soon we'll reach the oth-er shore, All in the ear-ly morn.

2. The waves are still and blue the sky, All in the ear-ly morn-ing. Our hearts are free, our spir-its high, Ev-'ry-one's gay this morn-ing. Our gon-do-lier will know the way, All in the ear-ly morn-ing, And then we'll have our hol-i-day, All in the ear-ly morn.

70

PEGGY

Jane Landon

Harvey Worthington Loomis

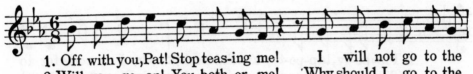

1. Off with you, Pat! Stop teas-ing me!   I   will not go to the
2. Will you go on! You both-er me!   Why should I   go to the

fair!_   Some oth - er col - leen can   be danc-ing with you. I
fair?_   But Brid - get and No-rah both like you and so— I

won't!   So   there!
might   be   there.

AND PAT

1. Come, Peg, the fair's be-gin-ning, With
2. Come, Peg, I'll not   be wait-ing. Ei-

fid - dlers tun-ing and pip - ers croon-ing. So   far I've seen No
leen   is pret - ty and Kate is wit - ty. They catch one's eyes, So

oth - er col - leen, Be - cause I'll be danc-ing with you._
if you are wise, You'd bet - ter be danc-ing with me._

After you have sung each of these songs separately, try
having two groups sing both songs at the same time.

THE SENSITIVE SERENADER

J. Lilian Vandevere

Italian Folk Tune

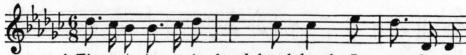

1. Tip-pe-ty, tap-pe-ty, knock, knock, knock, I come for to
   Tip-pe-ty, tap-pe-ty, knock, knock, knock, Please note the at-
2. Tip-pe-ty, tap-pe-ty, knock, knock, knock, Quite soon I shall
   Tip-pe-ty, tap-pe-ty, knock, knock, knock, Now are you a-

ser- -e-nade you.
ten-tion paid you.   When I am a-wake to trill and cheep,
be com-plain-ing.
wake or feign-ing?   I've war-bled my best in ev-'ry key,

Then how can you lie and blithe-ly sleep? Of course, there's a
Not one will un-lock your heart for me. This con-cert of

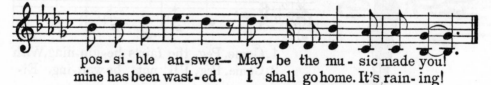

pos-si-ble an-swer— May-be the mu-sic made you!
mine has been wast-ed.   I shall go home. It's rain-ing!

In your singing, do you bring out the unevenness of the rhythm ♪. ♪♪ ♪. ♪♪
in the first measure and the smoothness of the first measure after the repeat?

A FRIEND IN NEED

Old Irish Rhyme

Old Irish Harper's Tune

Not too slowly

1. Spare   a   pen- ny   out o' your purse; The
2. Winds blow cru- el   o - ver the moor, And

72

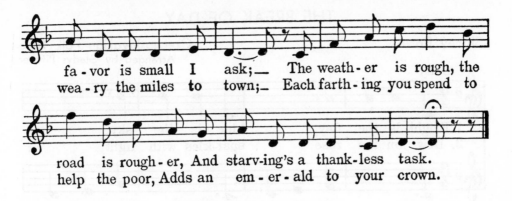

fa - vor is small I ask;___ The weath - er is rough, the
wea - ry the miles **to** town;___ Each farth - ing you spend to

road is rough - er, And starv - ing's a thank - less task.
help the poor, Adds an em - er - ald to your crown.

RIDE A SEA HORSE

Ernestine Evans   Mary Root Kern

Fast, with vigor

Ride a sea horse and ride a sea po - ny, O - ver the sea shelves,

rough and ston - y. O, how they tum - ble, lit - tle sea bron - chos,

When the waves rum - ble, when the wind blows. Dash - ing in un - der,

dart - ing up o - ver, On with the kel - pies, wild sea rov - er,

Light as a bub - ble, leap - ing and turn - ing, When the waves rum - ble,

when the wind blows,_____ when the wind blows.___

THE BREAK OF DAY

Sidney Rowe

Czechoslovakian Folk Tune
Arranged by Gladys Pitcher

1. Bright is the day, blue is the sky,
2. Dew on the rose spar-kles with light,

1. Bright, bright is the morn, blue the sky,
2. Dew, dew on the rose spar-kles, And

1. Wel-come an-oth-er fair day;_____ Sweet-ly the
2. Fresh is the wind from the west;_____ Morn-ing is

1. Wel-come an-oth-er fair day, we will wel-come the day;
2. fresh is the wind from the west, fresh the wind from the west;

1. lark, soar-ing on high, Sings us his beau-ti-ful
2. come, gone is the night, Earth now a-wakes from her

1. Sweet-ly the lark, soar-ing high, Sings us his beau-ti-ful
2. Morn-ing is come, gone is night, Earth now a-wakes from her

74

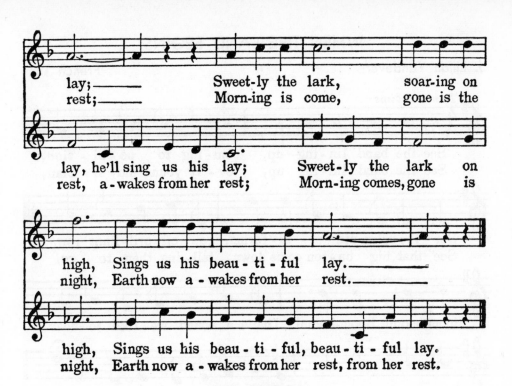

lay;——— Sweet-ly the lark, soar-ing on
rest;——— Morn-ing is come, gone is the

lay, he'll sing us his lay; Sweet-ly the lark on
rest, a-wakes from her rest; Morn-ing comes, gone is

high, Sings us his beau-ti-ful lay.———
night, Earth now a-wakes from her rest.———

high, Sings us his beau-ti-ful, beau-ti-ful lay.
night, Earth now a-wakes from her rest, from her rest.

THE BROOM
(De Bezem)

Translated by J. L. V.   Dutch Round

1. The be - som, the be - som, Oh, what is it for,
Dutch 2. De be - zem, de be - zem, Wat doe je er mee,
Pronunciation 3. Da bay - zum, da bay - zum, Wat doo ya air may,

Oh, what is it for? For sweep-ing, of course,
Wat doe je er mee? Wij ve - gen er mee,
Wat doo ya air may? Wye vay - hen air may,

For sweep-ing, of course, On your floor, and my floor.
Wij ve - gen er mee, De vloer aan, de vloer aan.
Wye vay - hen air may, Da vluur on, da vluur on.

A "besom" is a twig broom.

75

WHEN THE BAND BEGINS

J. Lilian Vandevere

French Tune

In march time

See the band lin-ing up, com-ing to po-si-tion,
See the band lin-ing up, ev-'ry young mu-si-cian,

See the splen-did u-ni-forms, row on bril-liant row.
See that big ba-ton come down, tell-ing them to go.

Boom-boom! Boom-boom! That's a sound we like to hear.

Boom-boom! Boom-boom! Mu-sic to a march-er's ear. Oh!

Swing down the street, eyes a-head and full of spar-kle,

Drums mark the time for a march-ing team that wins.

Dress right and make it smart, mark-ing time to-geth-er. Left, right and

then we start, when the band be-gins. Oh! when the band be-gins.

HIDING

Harvey Worthington Loomis

Anton Rubinstein

Lightly

1. When I call in the woods, and I'm all a - lone, Some-one
2. How I wish I could see who it is that sings, With a

else al-ways calls in the self - same tone. It is loud,___
voice like a boy's, yet he must have wings, For he hides___

then it's soft,___ Mock - ing all I
out of sight,___ Then he flies a -

say;___ It is loud___ then it's soft,___
way;___ Yes he hides___ out of sight,___

Mock - ing all (mock-ing all) I___ say.
Then_ he flies (then he flies) a - way.

77

WHEN BONITA DANCES

H. F.

Portuguese Tune
Arranged by G. P.

1.&2. When Bon - i - ta danc - es by,___ Ev-'ry boy in the
___ like to catch her eye,___ And he . . .

town will stand still.___ He would fer-vent-ly hopes that he will.___

1. In the folds of her hol - i - day shawl,___
She is nod-ding a greet-ing to all.___
2. There is some-thing that strong-ly ap - peals___ When Bon-i - ta
In the click of her ti - ny red heels.___

danc - es by___ She's the love-li - est girl in Bra - zil.___

THE JOTA

J. L. V.

Spanish Tune
Arranged by G. P.

Gaily

1. There's a dance that is gay in As - tu - ri - as,
2. Oh the danc - ers all think it a par - a - gon,

And they play this gay dance on ban - dur - ri - as,
And they're danc - ing it still up in Ar - a - gon.

With a click, light and crisp, from the cas-ta-nets;
It be-gan long a-go, but will still re-main,

Oh, the *jo-ta, one nev-er for-gets.___
Will the jo-ta, this old dance of Spain.___

*Pronounced "hō-ta."

ROSARIO

Stephen Fay

Portuguese Tune
Arranged by H. W. L.

In tango time

1. Ro-sa-ri-o can dance the tan-go As
2. Her smile is like the sun-shine beam-ing, Her

Sing "La, la, la, la," etc. *(click castanets if you like)*

grace-ful as a fawn could be, And when she trips the
man-ner is de-mure and shy; Her eyes of brown are

old fan-dan-go, As light as a bird is she.
bright-ly gleam-ing Like stars in the ev-'ning sky.

79

WHEN THAT I WAS AND A LITTLE TINY BOY

William Shakespeare
(in *Twelfth Night*)

Joseph Vernon (1738-1782)

1. When that I was and a lit-tle ti-ny boy,
2. But when I came to__ man's es - tate, With
3. A great while a - go the__ world be - gun,

A fool-ish thing was

hey, ho! the wind and the rain, 'Gainst knaves and thieves men
But that's all one, ou...

but a toy, For the rain it rain-eth ev-'ry day.
shut their gate, For the rain it rain-eth ev-'ry day. With
play is done, And we'll strive to please you ev-'ry day.

hey, ho! the wind and the rain, For the

rain it rain-eth ev-'ry day.

COME, LOVELY MAY

Chr. Ad. Overbeck
Translated by A. A.

Wolfgang Amadeus Mozart

Brightly

1. Dear May, we're done with snow-ing, Let green leaves bud and
2. When mild - er breeze is wing-ing, When new green springs each

80

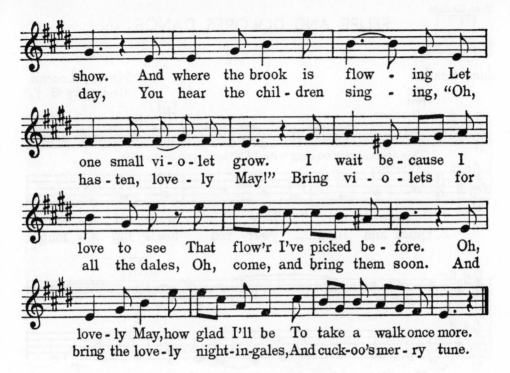

show. And where the brook is flow - ing Let
day, You hear the chil - dren sing - ing, "Oh,

one small vi - o - let grow. I wait be - cause I
has - ten, love - ly May!" Bring vi - o - lets for

love to see That flow'r I've picked be - fore. Oh,
all the dales, Oh, come, and bring them soon. And

love - ly May, how glad I'll be To take a walk once more.
bring the love - ly night - in - gales, And cuck - oo's mer - ry tune.

WINDY NIGHTS

Robert Louis Stevenson   Harvey Worthington Loomis

Mysteriously

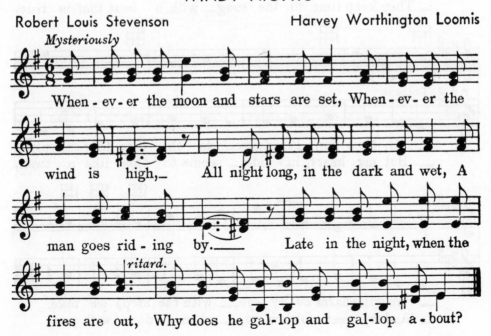

When - ev - er the moon and stars are set, When - ev - er the

wind is high,__ All night long, in the dark and wet, A

man goes rid - ing by.__ Late in the night, when the

ritard.

fires are out, Why does he gal - lop and gal - lop a - bout?

FELIPE AND DOLORES DANCE

Jane Landon

Harvey Loomis
Descant by G. P.

This descant may be sung with "Ah" or played on a violin.

FELIPE

1. Dance with me,___ here I wait all a - lone.___
2. Quick and light___ your red heels tap a - long.___

___ Hear the soft, mel-low tone___ of gui - tars that a - wake.
___ They keep time to the song___ with a beat that is true.

DOLORES

___ Si, Se - ñor, I'll dance___ to the tune they sup - ply.___
___ But my heart, in - side,___ seems to float like a swan,

___ We will charm ev - 'ry eye___ with the steps we take.
___ And my feet fol - low on,___ when I dance with you.

Our Country

"... from sea to shining sea ..."

TRAVELER'S LUCK

George Frederick McKay   George Frederick McKay

1. Spin the start-er turn the crank, Oil the gears and fill the tank,
2. Hip hur-ray! we're off a-gain, On to Far-go and Cheyenne,
3. Os-ka-loo-sa, here we go, Boi-se Cit-y, I-da-ho;
4. We won't skip New England's shore, Plymouth Town and Sagamore,

We are on our way to-day, Out up-on the broad high-way.
Take a side-trip on the way, Wich-i-ta and San-ta Fé;
On our way some fun to seek, In Du-luth and Bat-tle Creek.
Mas-sa-so-it, Marston's Mill, Chat-ham Beach and Os-ter-ville;

Off to try the tour-ist shan-ty In De-troit and
Hear our horns go "oo-ga, oo-ga" When we sail through
We shall wear the gay som-bre-ro When we reach A -
Pro-vince-town and old Nan-tuck-et, Pro-vi-dence, like -

Yp-si-lan-ti, Off to try the lodg-ings clas-sy,
Chat-ta-noo-ga, Al-so hear our fen-ders rat-tle
tas-ca-de-ro, We shall bask in breez-es balm-y
wise Paw-tuck-et, Glouces-ter where they catch such odd fish,

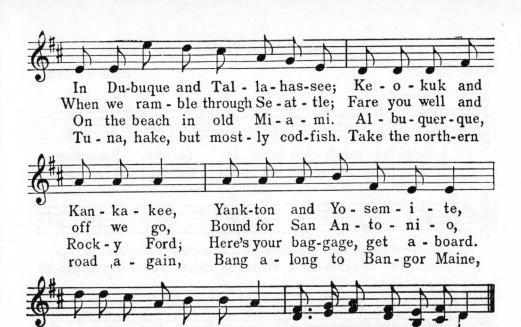

In Du-buque and Tal-la-has-see; Ke-o-kuk and
When we ram-ble through Se-at-tle; Fare you well and
On the beach in old Mi-a-mi. Al-bu-quer-que,
Tu-na, hake, but most-ly cod-fish. Take the north-ern

Kan-ka-kee, Yank-ton and Yo-sem-i-te,
off we go, Bound for San An-to-ni-o,
Rock-y Ford; Here's your bag-gage, get a-board.
road a-gain, Bang a-long to Ban-gor Maine,

All a-long the broad high-way, Thro' the grand old U. S. A.

Can you write other verses about other sections of our country? Can you substitute
the name of your own town for one of these, and find a rhyme for it, if necessary?

THE AIR LINER

Jane Landon   Harvey Worthington Loomis

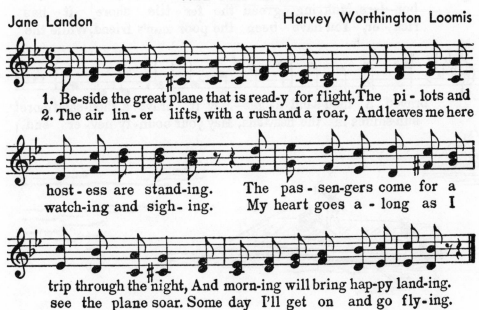

1. Be-side the great plane that is read-y for flight, The pi-lots and
2. The air lin-er lifts, with a rush and a roar, And leaves me here

host-ess are stand-ing. The pas-sen-gers come for a
watch-ing and sigh-ing. My heart goes a-long as I

trip through the night, And morn-ing will bring hap-py land-ing.
see the plane soar. Some day I'll get on and go fly-ing.

85

GREAT RIVER

David Stevens

Gladys Pitcher

Smoothly

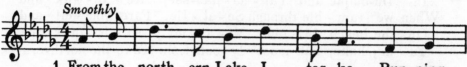

1. From the north-ern Lake I - tas-ka, Run-ning
2. No - ble riv - er, on your cur-rent You have

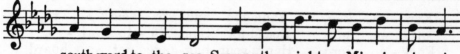

south-ward to the sea, Sweeps the might-y Mis-sis-sip-pi,
borne a mil-lion craft, From the swift-ly mov-ing steamboat

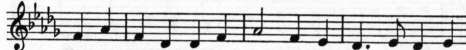

Flow-ing full and flow-ing free. Bear-ing life a - long its
To the slow and hum-ble raft. You have made the mar-kets

bor-ders, Mak-ing green the fer - tile shore, It has
rich - er, You have been the poor man's friend, While the

braved a thou-sand a - ges—May it brave a thou-sand more!
sun-shines in the heav-ens, May your boun-ty nev - er end.

With two sweeps in a measure
REFRAIN

Roll, Mis-sis-sip-pi, roll on! Proud and state-ly
riv-er, Fa-ther of Wa-ters, roll on!
Free and boun-teous giv-er. Count-less your blessings to
man, Source of life and plen-ty. On-ward, and nev-er stay,
Cease-less by night and day, Roll on!

The Mississippi is the largest river in the United States, and is known as the "Father of Waters."

THE HUDSON RIVER

David Stevens   Peter W. Dykema

With a stately swing

1. In the blue Ad-i-ron-dack moun-tains, Where the Hud-son
2. Since the days of bold Hen-ry Hud-son, He who gave our

Riv-er was born, Where Lake Tear-of-the-Clouds, in its beauty,—
riv-er its name, It be-came a great high-way of commerce,

(Hurring a little)

Re-flects all the col-ors of morn.— It starts with a
And just-ly en-ti-tled to fame.— It flows by the

rush-ing and tum-bling, Mak-ing rap-ids and falls as it
moun-tains of Cats-kill, Thro' the High-lands it press-es its

(Broadly again)

goes,— Till at last it be-comes a great riv-er,—Where the
way,— By the Pal-i-sades, mar-vels of beau-ty,— To the

tide from the o-cean flows,— Till at last it be-
wa-ters of New York Bay,— By the Pal-i-sades,

Hold back a little

comes a great riv-er,—Where the tide from the o-cean flows.
mar-vels of beau-ty,— To the wa-ters of New York Bay.

88

THE RIVER CHARLES

David Stevens

Roy S. Stoughton

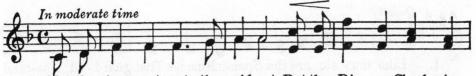

In moderate time

1. Not the long-est, not the wid-est, But the Riv-er Charles is
2. Then the white man saw the riv-er, And the shores he made his
3. It was thus the wind-ing riv-er, On its way to meet the

great, For its his-to-ry is wov-en With the an-nals
own, There he plant-ed seeds of progress And he reaped where
sea, Was the stream of life to he-roes Who were fight-ing

of a state. On its shores the proud Al-gon-quin Knew but
he had sown. Up and down the un-known val-ley Ranged the
to be free. At its source 'twas but a stream-let, Yet its

lit-tle then of strife, And this wind-ing, ram-bling riv-er
hard-y pi-o-neers, But they nev-er left the riv-er
pas-sage we can trace Till it grows to full com-plete-ness

1 & 2

3 *rit.*

Was to him the stream of life.
In those stern and try-ing years.
Like the . . . . pro-gress of our race.

Early towns grew up on rivers, because people could so easily travel on them.
The Charles River was one of the first to be settled in early New England days.

MISSION BELLS

J. L. V

J. Lilian Vandevere

1. Like mu - sic are the Span-ish names That guard - ed sa-cred
2. Though grass grows in the clois-ter walk Where brown-robed pa-dres

al-tar flames,—San Ber-nard-i - no, San *Jo-se, Where In-di-ans
used to talk, High in the ru-ined arch-es hung, Are mis-sion

learned to kneel and pray. And still there sounds, clear and true, The
bells that once gave tongue. No more they sway, to and fro, But

old, old chant that the mis-sions knew,— O - ra pro no - bis!
ech-oes float from the long a - go,— A - ve Ma-ri - a!

·*Pronounced "hō-zay."

PACIFIC

Balboa was a sailor,
   An ocean he did find.
The water was so peaceful,
   He felt that it was kind.
He looked down from a craggy peak
   And saw the ocean's plain.
Because he was a Spaniard
   He claimed it all for Spain.

David Millier
Aged 12   *El Monte, California*

HAWAII

Tune Ukelele
G C E A

J. Lilian Vandevere

Hawaiian Melody
Arranged by G. P.

In moderate time

1 {
'Tis a   gar-den, that fair Ha-wai-ian   is - land, Where
_____ show-er is   smil-ing thro' the   rain-bow, And

2 {
There the moon-light is fall-ing thro' the   palm-trees In
_____ dis-tance, the blue Pa-cif - ic   mur-murs For-

man-go and jac-quer-an - da   bloom. Where a
mu - sic en-chants the twi-light . . . . . gloom
rip-ples that seem like gold-en rain.___ In the
ev - er a soft and low re - . . . . . frain.

Isle where ro - mance is   set in   splen - dor, Where
Land where the scent - ed breeze is   ten - der, In

moun-tains are lift-ing to the   blue.___
fan-cy we'll sail a - way to . . .   you.___

— 91 —

YOSEMITE

David Stevens

Charles Repper

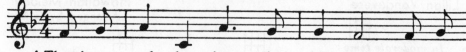

1. There's a val - ley, love - ly val - ley By Si -
2. There a - mong the domes of gran - ite That the
D.C. Oh, the po - ets sing of mar - vels In the

er - ra's west - ern side, Yo - sem - i - te, the peer - less,
fierc - est storms de - fy, "El Cap - i - tan," in gran - deur,
old world to be found; Of moun - tain peaks and cas - tles,

In its calm and state - ly pride, Its beau - ty rare, its
Reach - es up - ward to the sky. "Ca - the - dral Rocks," the
Songs of tri - bute loud - ly sound. But we will sing, with

mag - ic charm En - trance our won - d'ring eyes, And
"Broth - ers Three," And all that gal - lant band, Like
one ac - cord, Of won - ders rich and rare, The

rit.   *Fine*

there, the hand - i - work of time, This no - ble val - ley lies.
sen - ti - nels on end - less guard, These loft - y pil - lars stand.
home of beau - ty un - a - dorned; Yo - sem - i - te, the Fair.

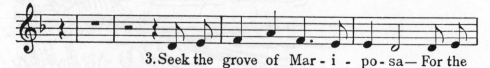

3. Seek the grove of Mar - i - po - sa— For the

gi-ant trees are there, The"Wash-ing-ton," "Wa-won-a,"

And the far-famed "Griz-zly Bear." The flow'rs that rich-ly

bloom are fed by falls that nev-er fail— The

wa-ters of "Yo-sem-i-te," And match-less "Brid-al Veil!" *D.C.*

THE SILO

Stephen Fay

Roy S. Stoughton

1. If you trav-el east or trav-el west Where far-mers till the ground,
2. In sum-mer-time we like sweet corn, To-ma-toes ripe and red.

You'll see in man-y farm-yards there A tow-er tall and round.
In win-ter we can't have them fresh, They come in cans in-stead.

That's where they store the win-ter food For cat-tle till the spring;
And so to feed his cat-tle well, The far-mer, he has planned

They call the tow'r a si-lo, 'Tis a ver-y use-ful thing.
For sum-mer food in win-ter, And he gives it to them canned.

American Heroes

"Let us now praise famous men . . ."— *Ecclesiastes*

DANIEL BOONE

Frederick Martens

American Tune
("The Girl I Left Behind Me")

Briskly

1. Old Dan-iel Boone, the pi - o - neer, He left a rep - u -
   ta - tion That ev-'ry-one must still re - vere, No
   mat - ter what his sta - tion. When Dan - iel was a
   boy at home, At farm-ing you'd not find him, A -
   hunt-ing in the fields he'd roam, And leave the plow be-hind him.

2. Old Dan-iel knew his way a-bout In re - gions all un -
   chart - ed; He al - ways knew the best way out, And
   fin-ished what he start - ed. The tribes pur-sued him
   night and day, To run him down and bind him, But
   Dan-iel al - ways got a - way, And left no trail be-hind him.

3. Old Dan-iel Boone, the pi - o - neer, For eight - y years and
   o - ver, He hunt - ed bea - ver, bear and deer, A
   fear-less fight-ing rov - er. He knew his trade with -
   out a doubt, No craft - y foe could blind him, He
   lived and died a fa-mous scout, And left his name be-hind him.

94

HAIL TO WASHINGTON!

R. W. G.   Robert W. Gibb

1. A hero we salute today,
2. He led his army through the war

Whose ev-'ry thought and deed He gave the people of the
That made our country free, And still that lib-er-ty en-

land In time of great-est need. All hail the name of
dures For all, for you and me.

Wash-ing-ton, His prais-es now we sing, A name that will for-

ev-er-more Throughout the a-ges ring. De-vot-ed to his

coun-try's cause, He nev-er sought for fame, And

still he lives in mem-o-ry, All hail his death-less name!

The picture above reproduces the mammoth group carved from the granite
face of Mount Rushmore, in South Dakota. This sculpture, by an American, Gutzon
Borglum, represents George Washington, Thomas Jefferson, Theodore Roosevelt,
and Abraham Lincoln. The design on the page opposite is from "The Spirit of '76,"
a painting by the American, Archibald M. Willard.

ABOUT ABE LINCOLN

George Frederick McKay   George Frederick McKay

Joyfully

1. Young Abe Lin-coln was lean and strong; He was hon-est the
2. Young Abe Lin-coln loved soil and sun; He loved laugh-ter and

whole day long; Young Abe Lin-coln de-serves a song, For
he loved fun; He loved work-ing till work was done, For

he loved all God's crea-tures. The wea-ry and op-pressed, The
he knew right and du-ty.

hum-ble and dis-tressed. From deep with-in came

kind-ness, With love he was pos-sessed. So

"of the peo-ple,

by the peo-ple,"

Land so wide and free! "By the peo-ple, for the peo-ple,"

Kept for you and me. God's pre-cious free-dom for-ev-er-more!

The wea-ry and op-pressed, The hum-ble and dis-tressed And
While still our ban-ner waves O'er land where none are slaves, His

all our chil-dren's chil-dren Shall call his mem'ry blest.
spir-it hov-ers, brood-ing, O'er con-se-crat-ed graves.

This beautiful statue of Abraham Lincoln was carved out of pure white marble by Daniel Chester French (1850-1931), for the Lincoln Memorial at Washington, D. C., (shown on page 96).

French was a great American sculptor. His first work, done while in his early twenties, was the famous "Minute Man" which stands in Concord, Massachusetts, and which was made after only a few lessons in the art, some of which he took from May Alcott, the original "Amy" in Little Women.

THE SAGE OF MONTICELLO

C. C.
Clinton Cole

Broadly

1. A song for Thom-as Jef-fer-son, He helped to found the
2. He played his well-loved vi-o-lin, When home in Mont-i-

na-tion, And set our in-de-pen-dence down, In a
cel-lo, And made that coun-try man-sion ring With his

fam-ous Dec-la-ra-tion. A fine Vir-gin-ia
mu-sic, soft and mel-low. Be-cause he stood for

gen-tle-man And a pres-i-dent, as well, He
gov-ern-ment, In a wise and sim-ple way, The

worked for real de-moc-ra-cy, A fact we're proud to tell.
name of Thom-as Jef-fer-son Is still be-loved to-day.

Thomas Jefferson was also a very clever inventor, an amateur artist, and an architect of note. He designed his beautiful home, Monticello, and built it on top of a mountain in Charlottesville, Virginia. His workmen cut the lumber, and made the nails and bricks right on top of the mountain.

THEODORE ROOSEVELT

Sidney Rowe   Gladys Pitcher

Sturdily

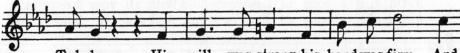

1. A rug-ged man was Roos-e-velt, The man his friends call
2. And yet his ear-ly youth was frail, But that he would not

Ted-dy;   His will was strong, his hand was firm, And
suf-fer;   His will took charge, till by and by No

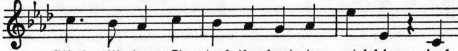

some-times rough and read-y.   His life was tire-less,
pine knot could be tough-er.   A les-son for the

filled with stress, It took the best to match him; And
young to learn,—Don't let mis-for-tune beat you, But

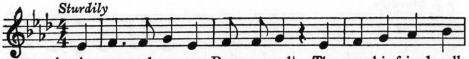

when he chose to mount and ride, No la-zy man could catch him.
cul-ti-vate the will to do, And noth-ing can de-feat you.

OUR INVENTORS

We honor all that Bell has done,
   And Whitney, Ford, and Wright,
McCormick, Howe, and Edison,
   Who ringed the world with light.
Among the men our land esteems
   Inventors claim their due,
Those men who visioned mighty dreams,
   And made their dreams come true.

J. L. V.

99

THE SAILING MEN

David Stevens

Peter W. Dykema

Sturdily

1. Oh, sing a song of sail-ing men, And make it loud and
2. Oh, sing a song of gal-lant Jones, And let it nev - er
3. Oh, sing a song of Law-rence bold, With all your strength and
4. Oh, sing a song of Far - ra - gut, And sing it loud and

strong! Oh, sing of ships and hearts of oak, Of all the daunt-less
die! Oh, sing of him whose sto-ried words Our an-nals glo - ri
will! Oh, sing of him whose cour-age high Sets all our hearts a -
clear! Oh, sing of him whose stead-y eye Could mark the course to

throng; The fear-less men who rode the sea To keep our na-tion's
fy;— Who fought the foe-man blade to blade And met dis-as-ter
thrill. In dy - ing words the Cap-tain brave A mot-to to our
steer. Who braved the mines of Mo-bile Bay, And by his dar-ing

ban-ner free, Who sailed and fought their wood-en craft, The
un - dis-mayed.'I'll nev - er yield nor take to flight, I've
Na - vy gave; Tho seized in death's re - lent-less grip, He
won the day, And through a rain of steel and lead, He

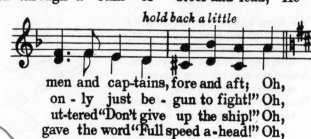

hold back a little

men and cap-tains, fore and aft; Oh,
on - ly just be - gun to fight!" Oh,
ut-tered "Don't give up the ship!" Oh,
gave the word "Full speed a-head!" Oh,

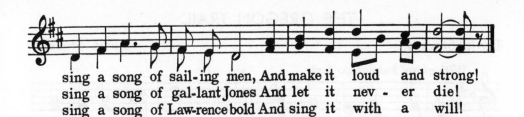

sing a song of sail-ing men, And make it loud and strong!
sing a song of gal-lant Jones And let it nev - er die!
sing a song of Law-rence bold And sing it with a will!
sing a song of Far - ra - gut And make it loud and clear!

HENRY BERGH

David Stevens   Charles Repper

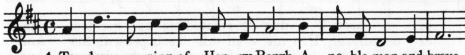

1. To - day we sing of Hen - ry Bergh, A no-ble man and brave,
2. He fought, des-pite un-friend-ly jeers And lack of help-ful laws,

Who lived a life of sac-ri-fice, Dumb an - i - mals to save.
Up - on his cho-sen bat-tle-field, A war-rior for his cause

The cru - el - ty of man to beast His soul could not a - bide;
At last, the hard fought strug-gle won, A new com-pas-sion came,

And then be - gan his great cru-sade With mer-cy as his guide.
Till now dumb crea-tures, could they speak, Would rise to bless his name.

Henry Bergh (1820-1888), a prominent and wealthy citizen of New York, devoted many years of his life and a large part of his fortune to a crusade against cruelty to animals. He met with much opposition but finally succeeded in organizing the American Society for the Prevention of Cruelty of Animals, from which grew the American Humane Society with branches throughout the nation.

THE OREGON TRAIL

David Stevens   David Stevens

With vigor, but not too fast

1. He stood and west-ward turned his eyes, The young and val-iant pi-o-neer; No dan-ger stayed his ea-ger feet, He did not know the name of fear. A long-ing for the se-cret world Be-yond the moun-tains dark and grim. The hope of new and bright-er dawns Pos-sessed the heart and soul of him.

2. His wife, with faith and cour-age rare, Com-pan-ion of his ar-dent dream, U-nit-ed all her hopes with his And saw with him the dis-tant gleam. The way was long, the ox-en slow, They plod-ded pa-tient by his side. One step— and then an-oth-er step And thus they crossed the Great Di-vide.

3. At last they reached their cho-sen goal, The val-leys of the great north-west. A land of prom-ise and of hope. And end-ed there a hope-ful quest. The days and years were some-times dark, Un-til there came the ra-diant dawn. The vi-sion re-al-ized by them Who dared the trail to Or-e-gon.

These verses were suggested by the experience of the pioneer, Ezra Meeker, who, as a young man, with his wife and baby, traveled the Oregon Trail and settled where the city of Puyallup, Washington now stands, and where he lived a long and useful life.

102

THE ALAMO

David Stevens   J. Meredith Tatton

Martially

1. Great deeds are re-cord-ed in his-to-ry's pag-es, Since
2. As long as the sto-ries of val-or are cher-ished, Re-

ev-er the world was young, Of he-roes whose names have come
mem-ber that no-ble_ band Who gal-lant-ly stood and as

down thro' the a-ges, By po-et and trou-ba-dours
gal-lant-ly per-ished, De-fend-ing their well-be-loved

sung. But near-er and dear-er each death-less name, Re-
land. Oh, sing of the he-roes, let bu-gles sound, Let

mem-bered with mourn-ful pride, Of the men, who with nev-er a
tear-drops be-dim the eye, For the men who for love of their

thought of fame, In the Al-a-mo fought and died.
sa-cred ground, In the Al-a-mo chose to die.

America Worships
"Our Father's God to Thee. . . ."

GOD OF OUR FATHERS

David C. Roberts

George W. Warren

(Three Trumpets)

1. God of our fa - thers,
2. Re - fresh Thy peo - ple

whose al - might - y hand
on their toil - some way;

Leads forth in
Lead us from

beau - ty all the star - ry band
night to nev - er - end - ing day;

Of shin - ing
Fill all our

worlds in splen - dor through the skies,
lives with love and grace di - vine,

Our grate - ful songs be - fore Thy throne a - rise.
And glo - ry, laud, and praise be ev - er Thine.

PRAISE GOD!

Jane Landon

Traditional Hebrew Melody

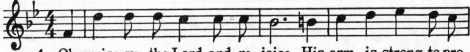
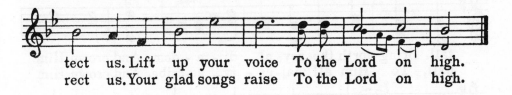

1. Oh, praise ye the Lord and re-joice. His arm is strong to pro-
2. The earth shall be filled with His praise. His care will guide and di-

tect us. Lift up your voice To the Lord on high.
rect us. Your glad songs raise To the Lord on high.

O GOD, BENEATH THY GUIDING HAND

Leonard Bacon

John Hatton

1. O God, be-neath Thy guid-ing hand
2. And here Thy name, O God of love,

Our ex-iled fa-thers crossed the sea;
Their chil-dren's chil-dren shall a-dore,

And when they trod the win-try strand,
Till these e-ter-nal hills re-move,

With prayer and psalm they wor-shiped Thee.
And Spring a-dorns the earth no more.

105

CORONATION

Edward Perronet

Oliver Holden

With dignity

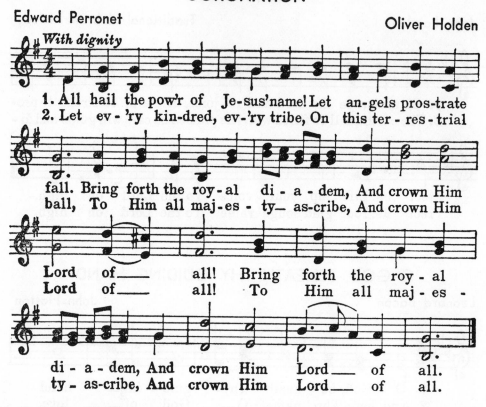

1. All hail the pow'r of Je-sus' name! Let an-gels pros-trate
2. Let ev-'ry kin-dred, ev-'ry tribe, On this ter-res-trial

fall. Bring forth the roy-al di-a-dem, And crown Him
ball, To Him all maj-es-ty_ as-cribe, And crown Him

Lord of___ all! Bring forth the roy-al
Lord of___ all! To Him all maj-es-

di-a-dem, And crown Him Lord___ of all.
ty_ as-cribe, And crown Him Lord___ of all.

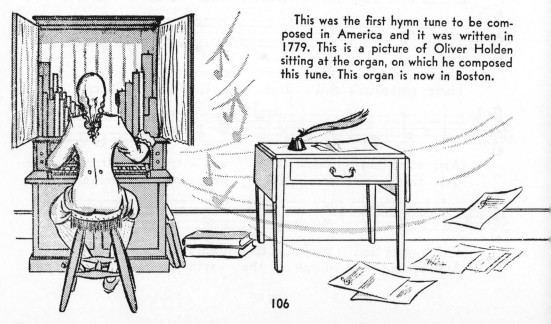

This was the first hymn tune to be com-posed in America and it was written in 1779. This is a picture of Oliver Holden sitting at the organ, on which he composed this tune. This organ is now in Boston.

WORK, FOR THE NIGHT IS COMING

Anna L. Coghill

Lowell Mason

Vigorously

1. Work, for the night is com-ing; Work thro' the morn-ing hours;
2. Work, for the night is com-ing; Work thro' the sun-ny noon;
3. Work, for the night is com-ing Un-der the sun-set skies;

Work while the dew is spark-ling; Work 'mid spring-ing flow'rs.
Fill bright-est hours with la-bor; Rest comes sure and soon.
While their bright tints are glow-ing, Work, for day-light flies.

Work while the day grows bright-er Un-der the glow-ing sun;
Give ev-'ry fly-ing min-ute Some-thing to keep in store;
Work till the last beam fad-eth, Fad-eth to shine no more;

Work, for the night is com-ing, When man's work is done.
Work, for the night is com-ing, When man works no more.
Work while the night is dark-'ning, When man's work is o'er.

A CHILD'S PRAYER

Dear God, I thank Thee for the day and night,
Both for the darkness and the light.
I thank Thee for the shining sun,
That watches over us while we have fun.
I thank Thee for the birds that come and sing
In summer and in spring.
I thank Thee for the pools where children wade,
I thank Thee for the trees that give us shade,
I thank Thee for the moon that shines so bright,
And for the stars that watch o'er us at night.

— Marilyn Yezner
St. Louis, Missouri

Aged 9

America Works

"I hear America singing, the varied carols I hear, . . .
The boatman singing what belongs to him . . .
The deckhand singing on the steamboat deck . . .
The woodcutter's song, the ploughboy's. . . ."

— Walt Whitman

SACRAMENTO

American Sailor's Chantey

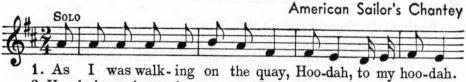

1. As I was walk-ing on the quay, Hoo-dah, to my hoo-dah.
2. Her hair was brown, her eyes were blue, Hoo-dah, to my hoo-dah.

A pret-ty girl I chanc'd to see, Hoo-dah, hoo-dah day.
Her lips were red and sweet to view, Hoo-dah, hoo-dah day.

Blow, boys, blow for Cal-i-for-ni-o. There's plen-ty of gold so

I've been told. On the banks of the Sac-ra-men-to.

3. I raised my hat and said "How do?"
   She bowed and said, "Quite well, thank you!"

4. I asked her then to come with me,
   Down to the docks my ship to see.

5. She quickly answered "Oh dear no?"
   "I thank you, but I cannot go?"

6. "I have a sweetheart young and true,
   And cannot give my love to you!"

7. I said "Goodbye" and strode away,
   Although with her I longed to stay.

8. And as I bade this girl adieu,
   I said that girls like her were few.

This song of the men who went by ship to California in the gold rush of 1849
is sung to a sailor's version of Stephen Foster's "Camptown Races." You will
find another gold rush song, to the tune of Foster's "Oh! Susanna" on page 130.

'WAY, 'WAY OFF ON GEORGE'S BANK

Frederic Manley

Charles Repper

1. Cap-tain Brown's my fa-ther's name and mine is Bil - ly Brown;
2. Fish-ing day and night for cod and mack-'rel when they run;
3. Win-ter time I go to school, be-cause I'm still a child;

"Lin - coln" is the schoon-er's and we hail from Glouces-ter Town;
Oh, but that's the time I love for that's the time for fun!
Geor - ge's Bank is aw - ful then, so an - gry, cold and wild;

Glouces-ter Town where moth-er waits and prays while we're a - way;
That's the time I steer and play I'm Cap - tain of the fleet,
How-ling for the lives of men whose fate may be to drown,

1 & 2

'Way, 'way off on Geor-ge's Bank, where we're fish-ing night and
'Way, 'way off on Geor-ge's Bank, when the winds blow warm and

1 | **3**

day.____ 'Way, 'way off on Geor-ge's
sweet.____

Bank, far from home in Glouces-ter Town.

George's Bank is the name of a fishing
ground in the North Atlantic Ocean.

109

PAUL BUNYAN

David Stevens   David Stevens

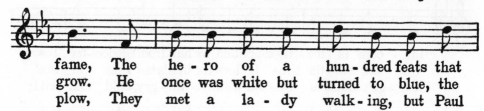

1. Oh, have you heard or read a-bout Paul Bun-yan, known to
2. Paul had an ox whose name was Babe; he nev-er ceased to
3. When Paul was dig-ging Pu-get Sound with Babe to pull the

fame, The he-ro of a hun-dred feats that
grow. He once was white but turned to blue, the
plow, They met a la-dy walk-ing, but Paul

lum-ber-jacks ac-claim? These tales re-late a-
Win-ter of Blue Snow. Four tons of grain he
nev-er stopped to bow, For she had waved her

maz-ing things a-bout the su-per-man, And
had to have for din-ner ev-'ry day; When
par-a-sol, a fright-ful shade of red, Which

when you hear them told or sung, be-lieve them if you
that was gone he just topped off with sev-'ral bales of
scared the Babe who ran a-way be-cause he lost his

Paul Bunyan is a "superman" of legend.
According to stories told all the way from
Maine to Washington and Oregon, he per-
forms marvelous deeds of great strength.

RED

(A few voices) Oh___ Paul Bun-yan,

can. Paul Bun-yan! Paul Bun-yan! He was twen-ty feet tall and
hay. Paul Bun-yan! Paul Bun-yan! It was all he could do, it
head. Paul Bun-yan! Paul Bun-yan! But he dug his right heel in

eight feet round, And when he walked he shook the ground. Paul
was, in-deed, When times were hard to pay for feed. Paul
sand and clay, And made a chan-nel deep that day. Paul

Oh___ Paul Bun-yan

Bun-yan! Paul Bun-yan! There was noth-ing he could not
Bun-yan! Paul Bun-yan! But he cher-ish'd his ox of
Bun-yan! Paul Bun-yan! With his won-der-ful ox of

do, For Paul he was a might-y man,
blue, For Babe he was a might-y ox,
blue, They ex-ca-vat-ed Hood's Ca-nal,

If all they say is true. *Hi!*
If all they say is true. *Hi!*
If all they say is true. *Hi!*

JOHN HENRY

Traditional   Negro Work Song

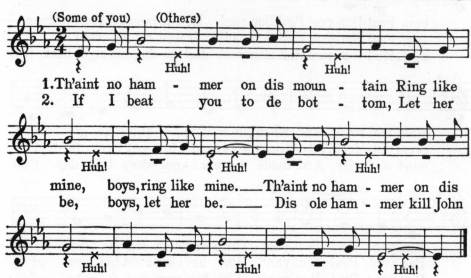

(Some of you)   (Others)

Huh!   Huh!

1. Th'aint no ham - mer on dis moun - tain Ring like
2. If I beat you to de bot - tom, Let her

Huh!   Huh!   Huh!

mine, boys, ring like mine.___ Th'aint no ham - mer on dis
be, boys, let her be. ___ Dis ole ham - mer kill John

Huh!   Huh!   Huh!

moun - tain Ring like mine, boys, ring like mine.___
Hen - ry, 'Twont kill me, boys, 'twont kill me. ___

John Henry is another imaginary character. Some of you
may like to swing an imaginary hammer and bring it
down on an imaginary rock pile as you say the rhythmic
"Huh!" Make it sound as if you were working hard!

THE NAVAJO BLANKET

Victor N. Pierpont   Navajo Indian Tune

1. Buy good In - dian Nav - a - jo blan - ket,
2. Buy good In - dian moc - ca - sin slip - per,

Col - or nev - er fade a - way;
Pret - ty la - dy like to wear;

Buy bead-work, sil-ver brace-let, Not much mon-ey have to pay.
Two bits can buy small bas-ket, She can car-ry ev-'ry-where.

"Two bits"—Western vernacular for twenty five cents.

BARKALINGO, WAHTERMILLION

South Carolina Street Cry   Adapted by Harvey Worthington Loomis

Bark-a-lin-go, wah-ter-mil-lion, wah-ter-mil-lion!

(Clapping) Jes' fum de vine, Ripe an' fine, Col' as ice an'

ber-ry nice. Bark-a-lin-go, wah-ter-mil-lion,

wah-ter-mil-lion! (Clapping) I load my gun wid'

su-gar-plum An' shoot de pret-ty gals, one by one.

Bark-a-lin-go, wah-ter-mil-lion,

wah-ter-mil-lion! (Clapping)

THE ERIE CANAL

Traditional   American Folk Song

Briskly, but not too fast

1. I've got a mule, her name is Sal, Fif-teen miles
2. We bet-ter get a - long our way,

on the E-rie Can-al,— She's a good old work-er and a
'Cause you bet your life I'd nev-er

good old pal, Fif-teen miles on the E-rie Can-al.—
part with Sal,

We've hauled some barg-es in our day, Filled with lum-ber,
Git up there, mule, here comes a lock, We'll make Rome 'bout

coal and hay, And we know ev-'ry inch of the way From
six o'-clock,— One more trip and back we'll go—

Al - ba - ny to— Buf-fa-lo.
Right back home to— Buf-fa-lo.

REFRAIN

Low bridge, ev - 'ry - bod - y down! Low bridge, for we're

go - ing thro' a town. And you'll al - ways know your neigh - bor,

poco rit.

You'll al - ways know your pal, If you ev - er

rit.

nav - i - gat - ed on the E - rie Can - al.

SHENANDOAH

Adapted   American Sailor's Chantey

With strong feeling

1. Oh Shen - an - doah, I long to hear you, And see your roll - ing
2. I long to see your smil - ing val - ley, And hear your roll - ing

riv - er; O Shen - an - doah, I long to hear you, 'Way
riv - er; I long to see your smil - ing val - ley,

We're bound a - way a - cross the wide Mis - sou - ri.

THE LONE STAR TRAIL

Traditional   Cowboy Song

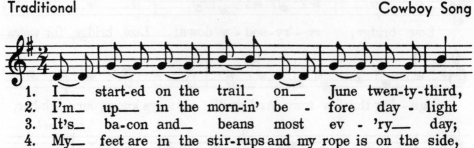

1. I__ start-ed on the trail__ on__ June twen-ty-third,
2. I'm__ up__ in the morn-in' be - fore day - light
3. It's__ ba-con and__ beans most ev - 'ry__ day;
4. My__ feet are in the stir-rups and my rope is on the side,
5. With my knees in the sad-dle and my seat in the sky,

I been punch-in' Tex-as cat _ tle on the Lone Star Trail,
And be - fore I'm a - sleep-in' the__ moon shines bright,
I'd as soon be a - eat - in' some prai - rie__ hay,
Just__ show me a horse_ that__ I can't ride,
I'll be punch - in'__ cows__ in the sweet by and by,

Sing-in' ki - yi yip-pi yap-pi yah, yap-pi yah, Sing-in'

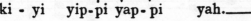

ki - yi yip-pi yap-pi yah.__

MEN AT WORK!

J. L. V.

J. Lilian Vandevere

1. Their un-i-form is o-ver-alls, And a shirt of hon-est
2. Their un-i-form is dun-ga-rees, That are splashed with grease and

blue, But they smile and wear it proud-ly, At the tasks they
oil, But they seem to march to mu-sic, As they start their

have to do. They ham-mer with a will, They work with skill,
day of toil. Just watch them as they go, And then you'll know

Build-ing fac-to-ries, homes, and schools. We give them a
What ef-fi-cien-cy real-ly means. We give them a

cheer, this ar-my of men, The men who work with tools.
cheer, this ar-my of men, The men who run ma-chines.

SONG OF THE WORKERS

"Chip! Chop!" our axes go,
Shaking the tree with a mighty blow.
"Chip! Chop!" our axes go.
Felling a tree is very slow.
Crash! Bang! It falls at last,
Soon it will be a big ship's mast.

Leslie Boyer
Palmyra, Missouri
Aged 10

117

America Sings

"... with my banjo on my knee ..."

I HAD FOUR BROTHERS OVER THE SEA

Traditional   Old Mountain Song

1. I__ had__ four__ broth - ers__ o - ver the sea.
2. The__ first__ sent me cher - ries with - out an - y stones.
3. The__ third sent a blan - ket with - out an - y thread.
4. When the cher - ries are in blos - som they have no__ stones.
5. When the blan - ket's in the fleece it__ has no__ thread.

Per - ri mer - ri dic - tum Do - mi - ne;

And they each__ sent a pres - ent__ un - to__ me.
The__ sec - ond sent a chick - en with - out an - y bones.
The__ fourth sent a book that__ could not be read.
When the chick - en's in the egg it__ has no__ bones.
When the book is in the press it__ can - not be read.

Par - tum quar - tum Pe - re - di - cen - tum,

Per - ri mer - ri dic - tum, Do - mi - ne.

THE GLENDY BURK*

Stephen Collins Foster   Stephen Collins Foster

With spirit

1. De Glen-dy Burk is a might-y fast boat Wid a
   I can't stay here for dey work_ too hard, I am
2. De Glen-dy Burk has a fun-ny old crew, An' dey
   De smoke goes up an' de in-gine roars An' de

might-y fast cap-tain, too; He sits up dar on de
boun'_ to leave dis town; I'll take my duds an' I'll
sing_ de boat-man's song; Dey burn de pitch an' de
wheel_ goes roun' an roun', So fare you well for I'll

1.
hur-ri-cane_ roof, An' he keeps an eye on de crew._
tote 'em on my back When de
pine_ knot, too, For to shove de boat a-long._
take a lit-tle ride When de

2.
Glen-dy Burk comes down.
Glen-dy Burk comes down.   Ho! for Lou'-si-an-a! I'm

boun' to leave dis town. I'll take my duds an'

tote 'em on my back, When de Glen-dy Burk comes down.

*The "Glen D. Burk" was the name of a river boat.

119

CLIMBING UP ZION'S HILL

Traditional
Extended by D. S.

North Carolina Mountain Song (extended)
Recorded by Gladys Pitcher

Oh, the heav-en bells are ring-ing and I'm go-ing home, And
I'm go-ing home. Oh, the heav-en bells are ring-ing and
I'm go-ing home, Climb-ing up Zi-on's Hill._ *Fine*

1. Oh, the joy-bells are ring-ing at morn-ing and night, Where the
2. Oh, they ring for the man-y, they ring for the few, When my
3. Yes, I'm go-ing to be there, my Lord tells me true, When my

D.C.

an-gels are stand-ing in gar-ments of white.
time comes I'll be there a-ring-ing them, too.
time comes I'll be there to sing hal-le-lu.

AT THE GATE OF HEAVEN
(A la Puerta del Cielo)

English version by A. D. Z.   Recorded in New Mexico by A. Armendariz
Arranged by Augustus D. Zanzig

Quietly

1. At the gate of Heav'n lit-tle shoes they are sell-ing
2. God will bless the chil-dren so peace-ful-ly sleep-ing,
1. *A la puer-ta del cie-lo Ven-den za-pa-tos,*
2. *A los ni-ños que duer-men Dios los ben-di-ce,*

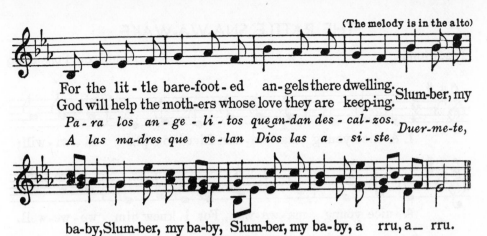

For the lit - tle bare-foot-ed an-gels there dwelling. Slum-ber, my
God will help the moth-ers whose love they are keep-ing.

Pa - ra los an - ge - li - tos que an-dan des - cal - zos. Duer-me-te,
A las ma-dres que ve-lan Dios las a - si - ste.

ba-by, Slum-ber, my ba-by, Slum-ber, my ba-by, a rru, a — rru.
ni-ño, Duer-me - te, ni-ño, Duer-me - te, ni-ño, a rru, a — rru.

This lullaby came over to this country from the Pyrenees Mountains in Spain.

MISTRESS SHADY

American Song

Gaily (The melody is in the alto)

O Mis - tress Sha - dy, — She is a la - dy, —
— She has a daugh - ter — whom I a - dore; — Each day I
court her, — I mean the daugh - ter, — Ev - 'ry
Sun - day, Mon - day, Tues - day, Wednes-day, Thurs-day, Fri - day,
Sat - ur - day, Sun-day af - ter-noon at half - past four. —

THE RATTLE SNA-WA-WAKE

Traditional

American Folk Song

1. A nice young ma - wa - wan Lived on the hi - wi - will;

A nice young ma - wa - wan, For I knew him we - we - well.

REFRAIN

To my rat - tle, to my roo - rah - ree.

2.
He scarce had mo-wo-wowed
Half round the fie-we-wield
Till up jumped—come a rattle come a sna-wa-wake,
And bit him on the he-we-weel. *Refrain*

3.
"O pappy da-wa-wad,
Go tell my ga-wa-wal,
That I'm a-goin' ter di-wi-wie,
For I know I sha-wa-wall."

4.
"O John, O Joh-wa-wahn,
Why did you go-wo-wo
Way down in the mea-we-we-dow
So far to mo-wo-wow?"

5.
"O Sal, O Sa-wa-wal,
Why don't you kno-wo-wow
When the grass gets ri-wi-wipe
It must be mo-wo-wowed?"

6.
Come all young gir-wi-wirls
And shed a tea-we-wear
For this young ma-wa-wan
That died right he-we-were.

7.
Come all young me-we-wen
And warning ta-wa-wake
And don't get bi-wi-wit
By a rattle sna-wa-wake.

ALL THE PRETTY LITTLE HORSES

Traditional

Negro Song

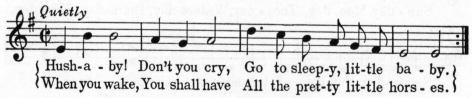

Quietly

{ Hush-a - by! Don't you cry, Go to sleep-y, lit-tle ba - by.}
{ When you wake, You shall have All the pret-ty lit-tle hors - es.}

Blacks and bays, Dap-ples and grays, Coach and six-a lit-tle hors - es.

Hush-a - by! Don't you cry, Go to sleep-y, lit-tle ba - by.

THE LITTLE PIG

Traditional   Vermont Folk Song

1. There was an old wom-an and she had a lit-tle pig,—
2. This lit-tle old wom-an kept the pig-gy in the barn,—
3. This lit-tle old wom-an fed the pig-gy on__ clo-ver,
4. Now that is the sto-ry of the pig-gy and the dame,

Mm___ Mm___ There was an old wom-an and she
Mm___ Mm___ This lit-tle old wom-an kept the
Mm___ Mm___ This lit-tle old wom-an fed the
Mm___ Mm___ Now that is the sto-ry of the

had a lit-tle pig,— He did-n't cost much 'cause he
pig-gy in the barn, The pret-ti-est thing she__
pig-gy on__ clo-ver, And when__ he died he__
pig-gy and the dame, And which of the two was the

was-n't ver-y big,— Mm.___
had__ on the farm, Mm.___
died__ all__ o-ver, Mm.___
most__ to__ blame? Mm.___

123

THE YEAR OF JUBILO

David Stevens

Henry C. Work

Brightly

1. { O com-rades have you seen the ban-ners that are
   { Now young and old, they join the cho-rus of the
2. { O chil-dren, there's a right good fel-low and he
   { For life, we know, is well worth liv-ing, and be

float-ing in the air? And have you heard the
best old song we know, A— song that's called "A
lives next door to you, 'Twill do you good to -
sure you make it so, For that's what makes the

sound of sing-ing in the na-tion ev-'ry-where?
good time com-ing in the year of Ju - bi - lo!"
mor-row morn-ing if you give him "How-d'- do!"
good time com-ing in the year of Ju - bi - lo!

REFRAIN

Don't you look be - hind, Look straight a - head,

ho! ho! For it must be now there's a

good time com-ing in the year of Ju - bi - lo!

WAIT, OLD MULE

Adapted by David Stevens

Early American Tune
("Old Tare River")

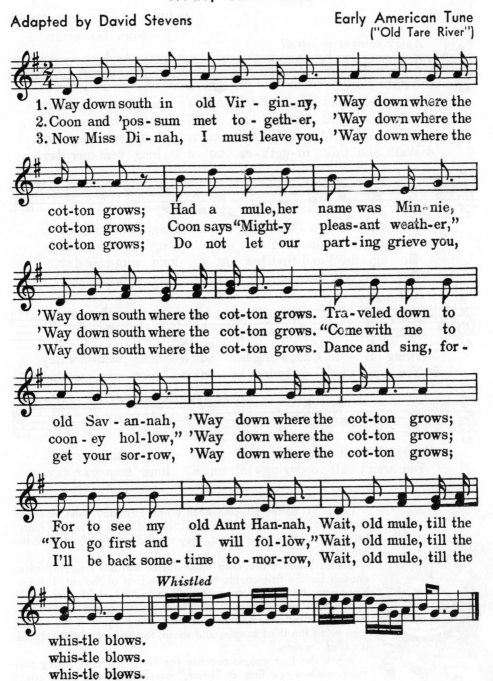

1. Way down south in old Vir-gin-ny, 'Way down where the cot-ton grows; Had a mule, her name was Min-nie, 'Way down south where the cot-ton grows. Tra-veled down to old Sav-an-nah, 'Way down where the cot-ton grows; For to see my old Aunt Han-nah, Wait, old mule, till the whis-tle blows.

2. Coon and 'pos-sum met to-geth-er, 'Way down where the cot-ton grows; Coon says "Might-y pleas-ant weath-er," 'Way down south where the cot-ton grows. "Come with me to coon-ey hol-low," 'Way down where the cot-ton grows; "You go first and I will fol-low," Wait, old mule, till the whis-tle blows.

3. Now Miss Di-nah, I must leave you, 'Way down where the cot-ton grows; Do not let our part-ing grieve you, 'Way down south where the cot-ton grows. Dance and sing, for-get your sor-row, 'Way down where the cot-ton grows; I'll be back some-time to-mor-row, Wait, old mule, till the whis-tle blows.

Whistled

125

SWEETHEART OUT A-HUNTING

A "Play Party" Folk Game
from Tennessee

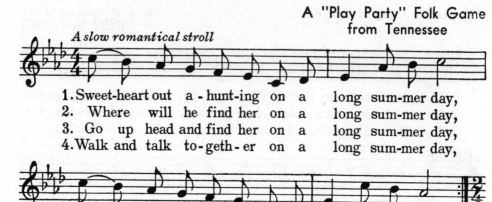

A slow romantical stroll

1. Sweet-heart out a-hunt-ing on a long sum-mer day,
2. Where will he find her on a long sum-mer day,
3. Go up head and find her on a long sum-mer day,
4. Walk and talk to-geth-er on a long sum-mer day,

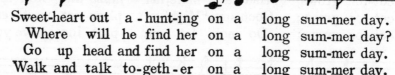

Sweet-heart out a-hunt-ing on a long sum-mer day.
Where will he find her on a long sum-mer day?
Go up head and find her on a long sum-mer day.
Walk and talk to-geth-er on a long sum-mer day.

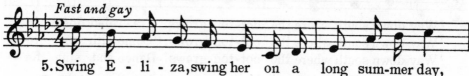

Fast and gay

5. Swing E-li-za, swing her on a long sum-mer day,
6. You aren't half a-swing-in' on a long sum-mer day,

Repeat as often as necessary for action

Swing E-li-za, swing her on a long sum-mer day.
You aren't half a-swing-in' on a long sum-mer day.

Two lines, partners facing each other. First boy walks slowly to the foot of the set and back, until the 3rd verse when he "finds" his partner. With arms linked, they stroll down and back until the 5th verse.

Verses 5 and 6 are sung much faster and are repeated often enough for the first couple to reach the foot of the set. The first boy swings his partner once and a half around, right arms linked. She then swings the second boy while he swings the second girl, left arms linked. The first couple then swing again in the center, then swing the third couple, and so on, to the foot of the set. This is called "reeling."

When the first couple reaches the foot of the set, they stay there, while a new first, or "head," couple begin the game again.

WHEN YOUR POTATO'S DONE

English by J. L.

Louisiana Folk Song

1. Your baked po-ta-to's done, It's time to eat it, it's time to eat, Your baked po-ta-to's done, It's time to eat it, it's time to eat. Wheth-er it's baked just right, (my Zu-zet-te) Wheth-er it's sweet or white, (my Zu-zet-te) But-ter and eat it all, my la-dy, But-ter and eat each bite.

2. Your baked po-ta-to's done, It's time to eat it, it's time to eat, Your baked po-ta-to's done, It's time to eat it, it's time to eat. May-be it is too brown, (my Zu-zet-te) May-be you'd like to frown, (my Zu-zet-te) But-ter and eat it all, my la-dy, But-ter and eat it down.

America Dances

"Swing your partner . . ."

FOUR IN A BOAT

Originating in the Appalachian Mountains

1. Four in a boat and the tide rolls high, Four in a boat and the
2. Choose your part-ner and stay all day, Choose your part-ner and
3. Eight in a boat and it won't go 'round, Eight in a boat and it

tide rolls high, Four in a boat and the tide rolls high,
stay all day, Choose your part-ner and stay all day,
won't go 'round, Eight in a boat and it won't go 'round,

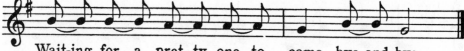

Wait-ing for a pret-ty one to come bye and bye.
We__ don't__ care__ what the old folks__ say.
Swing__ that__ pret-ty one__ you've just__ found.

The Dance

FORMATION—All join hands in a single circle, girl on the right of the boy. Two girls and two boys join hands and form a small circle inside of the other, facing the outside.

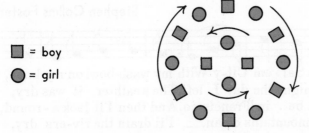

☐ = boy
○ = girl

VERSES—1   Outside circle skips to the left or clockwise, the inside circle goes opposite for sixteen counts or one verse.

2   Outside circle drop hands and march around in same direction while inside circle drop hands, choose partners in the outside circle and march beside them sixteen counts or second verse.

3   They now take their partners with them to form a larger inside circle and skip around as before but with a little more effort to suit the verse "and it won't go 'round." On the last line of third verse, all swing their partners, the tempo much accelerated.

Those who were in the center at the beginning now leave their partners to form the inside circle, and take their places in the outside circle.

Game is repeated as many times as desired.

OH! CALIFORNIA

When the bark "Eliza" cleared from Salem on November twenty-third, 1849, California bound, her men though not organized into a regular company had their own song. It was a parody of Foster's "Oh Susannah."

Stephen Collins Foster

1. I come from Sal - em Cit - y With my wash-bowl on my knee,
It rained all night the day I left, The weath-er it was dry,
2. I soon shall be in 'Francis-co, And then I'll look a - round,
I'll scrape the mountains clean, ___ I'll drain the riv-ers dry,

I'm going to Cal-i - forn - i - a The gold dust for to see.
The sun so hot I froze to death, Oh! brothers, don't you cry.
And when I see the gold lumps there, I'll pick them off the ground.
A pock-et full of rocks bring home, So brothers, don't you cry.

Oh! Cal-i - forn-ia ___ That's the land for me; I'm

going to Sac-ra - ment-o With my wash-bowl on my knee.

The Dance

FORMATION—Partners in single circle, all facing center, with girls on the right of boy.

☐ = boy

○ = girl

A—MEASURES— 1- 4 Girls take four steps towards the center and four steps backwards to place = 4 measures.

5- 8 Boys do the same = 4 measures.

B—REPEAT 1- 8 Grand right and left as follows:—face partner, boys
and on to facing counter-clockwise, girls facing clockwise, and
9-16 pass each other by taking first the right hand and then the left of persons walking towards you as you walk in your direction = 16 measures or 32 steps.

C—REPEAT 9-16 Promenade. Each boy takes the nearest girl approaching him, and with both facing counter-clockwise, walk or skip around circle in skating position, right hand in right, left in left and arms crossed.

Go back to part A and repeat as many times as desired.

S

131

GAVOTTE (1743)

Dr. Thomas Augustine Arne (1710-1778) (Adapted)

The Dance

FORMATION—Girl on the right of the boy, inside hands clasped and held high. Boys' outside hand on hip, girls' outside hand holding skirt.

■ = boy

● = girl

For one or more couples.

MEASURES— 1   Step on inside foot (girls' left foot, boys' right) point outside foot across (girls' right foot, boys' left) — 2 counts.
Repeat with other foot — 2 counts.

2- 3   Walk two steps forward beginning with inside foot — 2 counts.

"Balance step" forward and back by stepping forward on inside foot placing entire weight on it and at same time lifting the back foot slightly off the floor — 2 counts.

Step backwards on outside foot shifting the weight to that foot and at same time lifting front foot slightly off the floor — 2 counts.

Walk forward two steps beginning with inside foot — 2 counts.

4   Step on inside foot and point outside foot across. Hold
       position.

5- 8   Repeat same steps as in measures 1-4 starting with outside
       foot.

9-12   Partners still clasping inside hands held high do five "step
       points" as in measure 1 starting inside foot, moving clock-
       wise and finishing in each other's place in deep curtsy and
       bow.

       Dance may be repeated as many times as desired and may
       be danced around either in a circle or the length of the
       room.

The Gavotte was originally a peasants' dance and takes its name from Gap in
the old province of Dauphine, the natives being called "Gavots." It was introduced at Court in the 16th century, where, to amuse royalty, entertainments
were frequently given in national costume. About 1750 the dance was remodeled
to the taste of the period and brought back into fashion as a Court dance by
Marie Antionette, and from there to the other capitals of the world.

The picture shows the Gavotte being danced in the ballroom of the Governor's
Palace at Williamsburg, Virginia.

S

TURN, CINNAMON, TURN

Florida Folk-singing Game

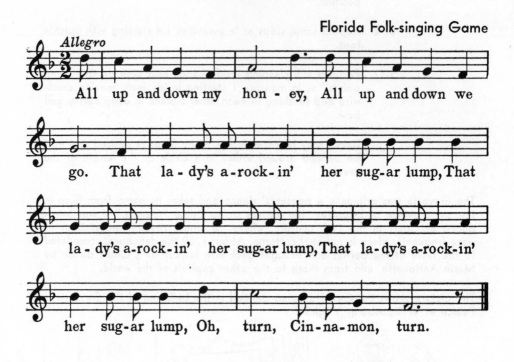

Allegro

All up and down my hon - ey, All up and down we go. That la - dy's a-rock-in' her sug-ar lump, That la - dy's a-rock-in' her sug-ar lump, That la - dy's a-rock-in' her sug-ar lump, Oh, turn, Cin-na-mon, turn.

The Dance

FORMATION—Boys choose partners. All stand in two lines, partners facing each other as for a reel.

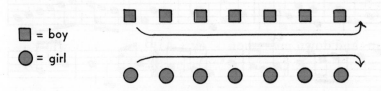

■ = boy

● = girl

MEASURES— 1- 4   Head boy takes his partner and slides four slides down and four slides back between the lines, boy finishing on girl's side and girl on boy's side.

5-12   While the others are singing—"That lady's a-rockin' her sugar-lump" they go down the line swinging each player and themselves in succession.* When they have finished swinging or "turning" all the players in the line, they take their places at the foot of the lines, the game or dance proceeding with the couple next in order and so on to the end.

*This step is called the "reel." See page 126 for directions.

MINUET (1788)

The Dance

FORMATION—Four couples in two straight lines, couple after couple. Girl on right of boy, inside hands clasped and held high.

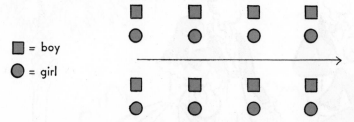

■ = boy

● = girl

A—MEASURES— 1- 2 Starting with inside foot, take three steps, one to each count, point outside foot out to the side, hold one count and place back beside the other foot.

3- 4 Repeat step starting with outside foot.

5- 6 Walk around slowly to each other's place with six steps, girl is now on the left of the boy, drop hands.

7- 8 Face each other, right hands clasped and held high. With right foot take one step towards each other,

136

drawing left foot up to right heel, three counts. **Step** backwards with left foot and make low bow or curtsy, three counts.

REPEAT—   1- 8   Steps are repeated from beginning, girl is now on the left of the boy.

B— MEASURES— 9   Inside hands clasped and held high. Start with outside foot, take one step forward and point inside foot forward, turning slightly away from partner so as to be almost back to back. Three counts.

                      10   Step on inside foot and point outside foot forward turning towards partner. Three counts.

                      11-12   Repeat with outside foot and inside foot.

                      13-16   First couple form arch with inside hands and walk backwards slowly as other couples pass through and also form arch and walk backwards.

                      17-24   Last couple is now at head of lines and steps are repeated from B, ending in single circle facing partner in low bow or curtsy.

REPEAT of B music:-

                      9-10   Take partner's right hand. Starting with right foot, take three steps passing partner and taking oncoming person's left hand, point left foot forward and hold.

                      11-12   Continue with left foot to next person, pointing right foot, holding right hand.

                      13-16   Repeat with right foot and left foot, finishing with bow or curtsy to partner, girls on outside of circle, boys inside.

                      17-24   First couple leads, others follow, from circle back into original two lines using same steps as in measures 1 - 8, finish with deep bow or curtsy.

Slow graceful movements should be used throughout.

The Minuet, "Queen of Dances," should be formal and stately. For about 150 years every State Ball opened with one. It originated in the Province of Poitou, France, and was introduced in Paris in 1653.

This would be a good tune to play on the violin or flute.

BROWN-EYED MARY

A song-dance of the Middle West

A If per-chance we should meet up-on the wide pe - rai-rie,—

In my arms would I em-brace my dar-ling brown-eyed Ma-ry.—

B Turn your part-ner half-way 'round and turn the **C** op-po-site la-dy.—

D Turn your part-ner in-to place and prom-e- **E** nade right hand la-dy.—

The Dance

FORMATION—Couples, lady at gent's right, face counter-clockwise and take hands in skating position, right hand over the left.

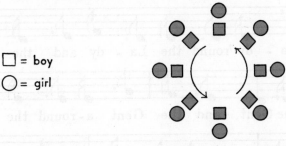

☐ = boy
◯ = girl

A—MEASURES— 1- 8   All skip around in circle, counter-clockwise, couple after couple, starting with the right foot—8 measures.

B—   9-10   Drop left hands only and with right hands still clasped, change places with four steps, finishing so that boy is facing clockwise and girl is facing counter-clockwise—2 measures.

C—   11-12   Drop hands and taking both hands of the person facing you, skip clockwise one complete turn using four steps or skips—2 measures, drop hands and

D—   13-14   in same way take partner's hands and continuing clockwise turn her to place, still skipping—2 measures, drop hands and

E—   15-16   moving forward counter-clockwise, the boy takes skating position with new partner—2 measures.

Dance is repeated with new partner.

LADY 'ROUND THE LADY

A Singing Quadrille

For it's La - dy 'round the La - dy and the

Gent a - round the Gent and the Gent a - round the

La - dy and the La - dy 'round the Gent.

Four hands half, ___ half ___ right and left.

Swing your La - dy once a - round and lead up to the next.

FIDDLER

The Dance

FORMATION—Four couples form a square set, girl on the right of the boy.

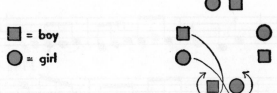

☐ = boy

⬤ = girl

MEASURES— 1- 2 While the others sing, the first couple leads over to the couple on their right and passing between girl and boy of that couple, the first couple cross each other (girl passing in front of her boy) so as to enable the "lady to go 'round the lady and the gent around the gent."

3- 4 They cross each other again and "the gent goes 'round the lady and the lady 'round the gent."

5 The two couples are now facing each other, join hands and circle half-way around to the left so that first couple is facing towards the inside of circle. ("Four hands half")

6 The two couples pass through each other, the girls pass left shoulder in the middle, the boys pass on the outside. ("Half right and left")

7- 8 First couple swings in the center of circle while the other couple swings in own place and finishes with girl on right of her boy again. ("Swing your lady")

REPEAT— 1- 8 First couple now leads up to the next couples in turn repeating from the beginning each time.

9-24 After dancing with the last couple, the first couple swing themselves back into their own place. Everyone takes his partner by the left hand and makes one complete turn in place counter-clockwise ("Allemande left") and then all do the Grand Right and Left or Chain, boys going counter-clockwise, girls clockwise.

Dance is repeated for each couple in the set.

S

RUSTIC REEL

19th Century American Dance

This is a nice old fiddle tune. Can someone play it on the violin?

The Dance

FORMATION—Boy with a girl on each hand facing a similar trio, all sets in one large circle to make action progressive, moving clockwise.

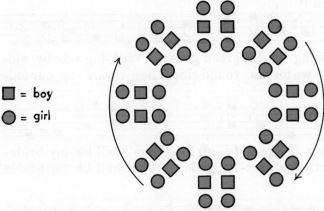

■ = boy

● = girl

A—MEASURES— 1- 8 Each boy takes opposite girl on his right hand and slide (or chassez) 8 slides to the right and 8 slides back to place = 8 bars.

B—REPEAT 1- 8 Boy now takes opposite left hand girl and slides 8 slides to the left and 8 slides back to place = 8 bars.

C— 9-16 All move forward and back with hands joined (four steps forward, 4 back), then move forward again and pass through to meet next set with whom dance is repeated = 8 bars.

KING and QUEEN

Florida Folk-singing Game

A and B

Walk-ing on the green grass, Walk-ing side by side,
And now we form a round ring, The girls are by our sides,

Walk-ing with a pret-ty girl, She shall be my bride.
Danc-ing with the pret-ty girls Who shall be our brides!

C Allegro

And now the King up-on the green Shall choose a girl to

be his Queen, Shall lead her out his bride to be, And

kiss her one, two, three.

D REFRAIN Moderato

Now—— take her by the
O—— swing the King and

hand, the Queen, And swing her 'round and 'round the green, And, oh,
swing the Queen, O, swing them 'round and 'round the green, O,

E

now we'll go a-round the ring And ev-'ry one we'll swing.
swing the King and swing the Queen, O, swing them 'round the green.

The Dance

Boys choose their partners as for a dance and then promenade as in a procession, singing: A—Walking on the green grass, etc.

The procession now forms into a single circle, girl to the right of the boy. Music is repeated, all singing: B—And now we form a round ring, etc.

Circle keeps moving during the stanza but forms into two lines as for a reel, girls in one line, boys in the other, at the end of the verse. Head couple are the King and Queen and do as the verse directs while the others sing: C—And now the King upon the green, etc.

REFRAIN—   D—Now——take her by the hand, this Queen,
                      And swing her 'round and 'round the green.

Having done so with the Queen, the boy begins with the second girl and so on down the line, swinging each girl in turn, while the Queen does likewise with the boys.

                E—And, oh, now we'll go around the ring,
                      And everyone we'll swing.

REFRAIN—   O——swing the King and swing the Queen, etc.

This verse is sung and repeated until all have been swung. The King and Queen are now at the foot of line and new head couple are now King and Queen. Song is repeated from the refrain until all have been King and Queen, then all promenade.

145

PIG IN THE PARLOR

This song-game is said to be 300 years old.

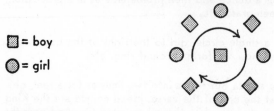

▣ = boy

◉ = girl

DIRECTIONS—One boy in centre of circle without a partner, while others form single circle with girls on the right of the boys. Moving clockwise in circle, all skip round singing:—

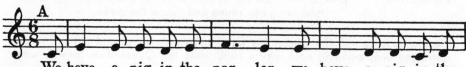

We have a pig in the par-lor, we have a pig in the

par-lor, We have a pig in the par-lor, and he is big and round.

Facing partners do as follows:—

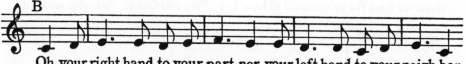

Oh, your right hand to your part-ner, your left hand to your neigh-bor,

And back a-gain to your part-ner and swing her 'round and 'round.

2nd VERSE—

    A—We have a pig in the parlor, we have a pig in the parlor,
      We have a pig in the parlor and he is on the floor.

    B—Oh, your right hand to your partner, your left hand to your neighbor,
      Your right to number three then swing with number four.

Odd boy in the center tries to take a girl just before they swing in either first or second verse and boy left without a partner is the "pig."

Our Good Neighbors–North and South

"We ought to do our neighbors all the good we can . . ."
— *Brahman Philosophy*

ROLL, MY BALL!
(En Roulant, Ma Boule)

Translated by J. L. V.   French-Canadian Folk Song

REFRAIN

Roll, my ball, keep roll-ing a-long. Roll my ball, keep roll - ing.

1. A pond be-hind my cot-tage lay,
2. There three fine ducks could swim and play,
3. The prince came by to hunt, one day,

Roll, my ball, keep roll - ing. There three fine ducks could
The prince came by to

cot - tage lay. There three fine ducks could swim and play.
swim and play. The prince came by to hunt, one day.
hunt, one day. His gun was sil - ver, so they say.

REFRAIN: En roulant, ma boule, roulant! En roulant, ma boule!
  1. Derrier' chez nous y'a-t-un etang, En roulant, ma boule!
     Derrier' chez nous y'a-t-un etang,
     Trois beaux canards s'en vont baignant.

  2 Trois beaux canards s'en vont baignant, En roulant, ma boule!
     Trois beaux canards s'en vont baignant,
     Le fils du roi s'en va chassant.

  3. Le fils du roi s'en va chassant, En roulant, ma boule!
     Le fils du roi s'en va chassant,
     Avec son grand fusil d'argent.

THE YOUNG VOYAGEUR

Oliver Orden

Canadian Voyageur Tune

Smoothly

1. From his home in the North Comes the young voy-a-geur,
2. There's a smile on the lips Of the young voy-a-geur,

His ca-noe lad-en well With a car-go of fur.
And the sound of his voice Sets the for-est a-stir.

Chill tho' the air, Naught should he care, For there's
Pad-dle keeps time, Sweet ech-oes rhyme, There's a

joy in the heart of the young voy-a-geur.
song in the heart of the young voy-a-geur.

THE BOAT GIRL
(La Barquillera)

Translated by J. Lilian Vandevere

Mexican Song
Arranged by G. P.

With motion

I sailed from a love-ly port one day, Where
En un de-li-cio-so puer-to Di

toss-ing waves rose wide-ly. A ti-ny boat rocked there
ver-de y fres-ca o-ri-lla. En u-na frá-gil bar-

148

i - dly___ And I took it to go a - way.___
qui - lla___ U - na tar - de me em - bar - qué.

But the maid - en___ who was row - ing___ watched with
Y la her - mo - sa___ bar - qui - lle - ra___ No ce -

tears the waves at play.___ Ah___
sa - ba de llo - rar,

And she said "How far they are
Por - que sen - tir li - bre qui -

___ Ah___

go - ing, Would that I were as free as they!"
sie - ra___ Co - mo las o - las del mar.___

149

THE MEADOW BROOK

Henry Snow   Peruvian Folk Tune

Quietly

1. Down the shad-owed lane, Be - side the brook-let I
2. Ti - ny flow'rs of blue, With yel - low cow-slips be-

stray, Its song is sweet_ to me,
tween, And al - ways grow - ing there,

There I'd like_ to be, all the day.
Ferns called maid - en hair, cool and green.

TUNEFUL TIM SAYS: Here are some rhythms you often hear. They are very much used, especially in Latin-American music. Can some of you tap them, or play them on tambourines, castanets or drums, while others count steadily in fours?

Try playing these rhythms to accompany these two songs.

MARGARIDA

Adapted by J. L. V.

Brazilian Folk Song

1. Mar - ga - ri - da seeks the foun - tain, Mar - ga -
2. Small but charm - ing is her dwell - ing, Small but

ri - da seeks the foun-tain with her jug of clay. Like the
charm-ing is her dwell-ing, you can find the street. There the

lil - ies on the moun-tain, Mar - ga - ri - da seeks the
songs of birds are swell-ing, While a - bout her charm-ing

foun-tain, Takes her sol - i - ta - ry way. Mar - ga - ri - da,
dwell-ing Blos-soms make her gar-den sweet. Mar - ga - ri - da,

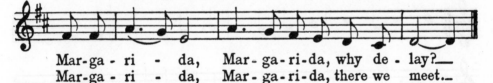

Mar-ga - ri - da, Mar - ga-ri-da, why de - lay?__
Mar-ga - ri - da, Mar - ga-ri-da, there we meet.__

Here are the Portuguese words. Can you sing them?

Margarida vai a fonte
Margarida vai a fonte,
   Leva a sua cantarina;
Brotam lyrios pelas montes,
Margarida vai a fonte,
   Vai a fonte e vem sosinha.
Margarida, Margarida,
Margarida vai a fonte.

E' tão linda a casa d'ella,
E' tão linda a casa d'ella,
   Fica a beira d'um caminho,
Os canteiros da janella,
Circulando a casa d'ella,
   Tem aroma a rosmaninho.
Margarida, Margarida,
Margarida vai a fonte.

TUNEFUL TIM SAYS: Here is a part of a tune called a *figure*: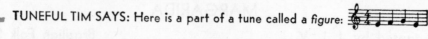

See how it can be repeated and moved up or down with a few other notes added, to make a longer tune (melody) —like this:

Do you notice how this melody divides, naturally, into two four-measure phrases?

A *figure* treated in this way makes what we call a *sequence*. This word means "following in an orderly manner." You will find a good example of this use of figures in "Morning Hymn" on page 7. Other examples are on pages 9, 10 and 31. Can you find still others?

Here are some more *figures*. Can you make tunes from them?

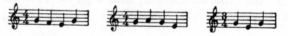

Sometimes you can use a figure upside down as well as right side up— such as this one:

The figure: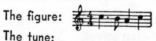

The tune:

Can you think of some other figures and make tunes from them?

This is part of a famous melody by Giuseppe Verdi, called the "Anvil Chorus." The repetition of the figure sounds like a *sequence*, but you will see that the figures are not always *exactly* the same.

I LIKE THE FALL

Dixie Willson

Roy Newman

In moderate time

1. I like the Fall the mist and all. I
2. I like to sit and laugh at it, And

like the night-owls lone-ly call, The
tend my co-sy fire a bit. I

wail-ing sound of wind a-round. I like the Fall.
like the Fall, the mist and all. I like the Fall.

COLUMBUS

David Stevens

Spanish Folk Tune

In moderate time

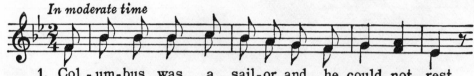

1. Col - um-bus was   a   sail-or and   he could not   rest
2. He sailed and sailed   but vain-ly looked for signs of   land;
3. When hope and strength and for-ti-tude were   al-most spent,
4. Col - um-bus thought 'twas In-di-a,   but   he was wrong,

Be-cause he thought that In - di - a   lay tow'rd the   west.

His crew be - came   a   dis-con-tent-ed,   sul-len   band.

A float-ing branch re-stored his faith and   on   he   went.

For   he had found A - mer - i - ca, now great   and strong.

Queen Is - a - bel - la   gave him gold for ships and   crew,

But when they cried; "O   Ad - mi - ral, for-sake thy   quest!"

A   shore-bird at   the   mast-head set his heart a - glow,

The   land where sa - cred Free-dom lives and holds her   sway;

And   off he sailed in   Au - gust, Four-teen nine - ty - two.

He stern-ly bade them hold their peace, and still   sailed west.

And then the look-out hailed the   deck and cried "Land-ho!"

And that is why we   cel - e - brate Col - um - bus   Day.

WIN!

Clinton Cole

Robert W. Gibb

In march time

Come, join the cheer-ing for the foot-ball game; Cheer for the

team that means to bring us fame. Come, set the ban-ners fly-ing,

Come, where the crowd is cry-ing, Hip, hip, hur-ray! It's

time to be-gin. Watch for the run-ner when the

ball goes through. Watch for a tack-le and a touch-down, too.

On, team, go on and meet them, Play, team, you must de-feat them,

Win, team, win!

A HALLOWE'EN HAPPENING

Clinton Cole   Peter W. Dykema

Mysteriously

'Twas a ghost in a sheet, and the ghost said, "Boo!" Such a

queer, scar-y ghost, in a gown of white. Then a witch came a-long,

and a black cat, too, But they both dis-ap-peared in the night.

That queer ghost came a-creep-ing, That queer ghost came a-peep-ing,

Much queer-er, much near-er, To snatch me, and catch me.

And I quiv-ered and I shiv-ered when the ghost said, "Boo!"

Yes I quiv-ered and I shiv-ered when the ghost said, "Boo!"

'Twas dis-tress-ing to be guess-ing what a ghost might do.

Then I saw that the ghost— was you!

TO THE FLAG

David Stevens

George W. Chadwick

1. The flag that is fly-ing in stain-less glo-ry, The
2. In years that are com-ing, what-e'er be-fall us, The

sign of a free-dom that ne'er shall die, It flies o-ver
Star-Span-gled Ban-ner shall be our guide. What-ev-er its

free-men, Whose fa-thers wrote our sto-ry, And flung their new-born
mis-sion, Wher-ev-er it may call us, We'll rise and fol-low

stand-ard to the az-ure sky!
where it leads with faith and pride!

Here come the col-ors

that we all hold dear! Greet Old Glo-ry with a rous-ing

cheer! Pre-serve its fair re-nown And nev-er let it down—

The Stars and Stripes for-ev-er stand for free-dom!

LANDSCAPE IN NOVEMBER

Helen Fitch

Stuart Bliss Hoppin

1. Bon - fires are burn - ing and blue smoke is lift - ing.
2. Brown fields are emp - ty where green corn was grow - ing.

Hear the lone crow as he calls (he calls).
As - ters have fad - ed a - way (a - way).

Chill wind is ris - ing and grey clouds are drift - ing.
Lead - en and i - cy the riv - er is flow - ing.

Si - lent and soft, a first snow - flake falls.
Pic - ture No - vem - ber in tones of grey.

THANKSGIVING

Adapted

J. B. Weckerlin

Brightly

When shades of dark-ness fly,— And morn's a-blaze on high,— We sing a glad Thanks-giv-ing For song, oh!— all the joy of liv-ing, For earth and sea and sky.—

On page 105 you will find a well-known Thanksgiving hymn.

DECEMBER TREASURES

J. L. V.

Russian Folk Tune

In moderate time

1. Dry brown oak leaves shiv-er in the wood-land,
2. No more fire-flies glim-mer in the twi-light,
3. No more moon-light, full of sum-mer mag-ic,

Not a bud or flow'r is seen; But in-stead of them,
Float-ing high or drift-ing low; But in-stead of them,
Shin-ing sil-ver, high and far; But in-stead of it,

gleam-ing cheer-i - ly, Shines the hol-ly wreath, gay and green.
soft - ly ra - di-ant, Christ-mas can-dle-light, all a - glow.
bright-ly beau-ti-ful Gleams the glo - ri - ous Christ-mas star.

CAROL OF THE CREATURES

J. Lilian Vandevere

German (1460)
Arranged by G. P.

1. On Christ-mas Eve when Je - sus lay all fast a - sleep__
2. The stur - dy ox be-held the Child in si - lent awe,__
3. The pa - tient don-key wait-ed there, all for to go,__

The crea-tures spoke, the first of them the gen-tle sheep.__
And said "I glad-ly of-fer him my bed of straw."__
To car - ry this, the lit - tle Lord, both to and fro.__

Ah_____ Ah_

"I give my soft-est wool to keep him warm.__ 'Twill
Doves, coo-ing gen-tly, spread their snow-y wings.__ The
Thus ev-'ry crea-ture had a gift to bring.__ To

make a swad-dling blan-ket that shall keep him from the win-ter storm."
faith-ful dog stood guard be-side the slum-ber of the King of Kings.
show their love and rev-'rence for the ba - by who was born their King.

OLD CHRISTMAS SONG

Translated by A. A.

Old Carol

Make each repetition an echo.

1. While by my sheep I lay a-wake,
God's an-gel came, to me he spake.
Now joy is mine.

Joy, joy, joy! Grant us thy bless-ing, Lord, we pray.

2. "Bethlehem seek before the light.
There shall a child be born tonight."

3. "Small though he lies within the stall,
He is the Lord to save us all."

4. When I beheld the Christ Child's face.
Scarce could I leave that holy place.

5. Well must I guard this gift divine,
Fullness of joy shall then be mine.

MARY'S LULLABY

David Stevens

Polish Carol

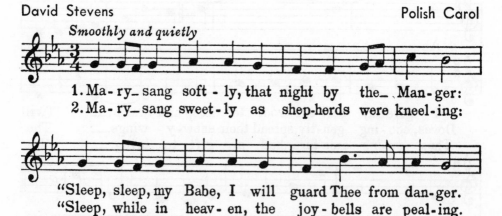

Smoothly and quietly

1. Ma-ry_ sang soft-ly, that night by the_ Man-ger:
2. Ma-ry_ sang sweet-ly as shep-herds were kneel-ing:

"Sleep, sleep, my Babe, I will guard Thee from dan-ger.
"Sleep, while in heav-en, the joy-bells are peal-ing.

An-gels, bright an-gels their night-watch are keep-ing."
Sleep Thou, till_ dawn o'er the moun-tain comes peep-ing."

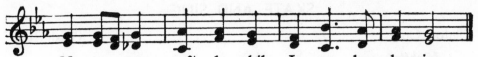

Ma - ry_ sang soft - ly while Je - su lay sleep-ing.
Ma - ry_ sang sweet - ly while Je - su lay sleep-ing.

GOD BLESS THE MASTER OF THIS HOUSE

17th Century English

William Peters

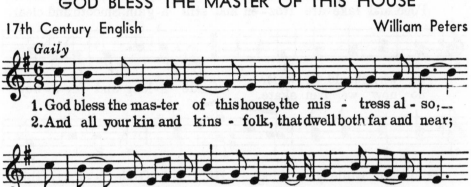

Gaily

1. God bless the mas-ter of this house, the mis - tress al - so,_
2. And all your kin and kins - folk, that dwell both far and near;

And all_ the lit - tle chil - dren that round the ta - ble go.
I wish you a mer - ry Christ-mas and a hap - py New_ Year.

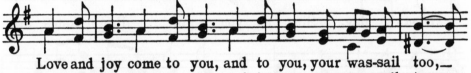

Love and joy come to you, and to you, your was-sail too,_
Love and joy come to you, and to you, your was-sail too,_

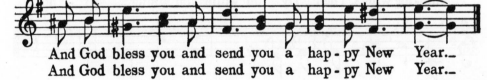

And God bless you and send you a hap - py New Year._
And God bless you and send you a hap - py New Year._

SKATE AND SING

Clinton Cole

Polish Tune

Lightly

Snow is deep, and white on the hill a-gain. Ice is thick,
Pond and lake are froz-en and still a-gain. Smooth and clear,

so why should we wait?
so now we can skate. Glide a-long and far a-way.

Glide on while you sing__ Hi - ho! Glide a-long, this

frost-y day, Sing as you go. Bright skates are

shin-ing wings, Then fly on while you sing__ Hi - ho!

Share the fun that win-ter brings. Sing as you go.

ST. VALENTINE'S DAY

William Shakespeare

Old English

Gaily

Good mor - row! 'tis__ Saint Val - en-tine's Day,__

All in the morn-ing time,— And I,— a maid at your

win - dow, To be— your val - en - tine.—

FEBRUARY FOURTEENTH

Mary de Haven

French Folk Tune (adapted)

Why not send a val-en-tine, a great big gay one,
D.C. Po-sies make a val-en-tine, a fra-grant sweet one,

Write up-on the en-ve-lope a friend's ad - dress.
Choose a po-sy val-en-tine for some dear friend.

Choose a flow'r-y val - en-tine, no ev - 'ry - day one,
Still, for just a nick-el, you can buy a neat one,

Fine

Nev - er, nev - er sign your name, but let her guess.
Just as nice a val - en - tine as one need send.

D.C. al Fine

Can-dy in a box, with a big red bow, Is a treat I know.

165

A SONG FOR EASTER

Adapted by Jane Landon

Lowell Mason (1840)

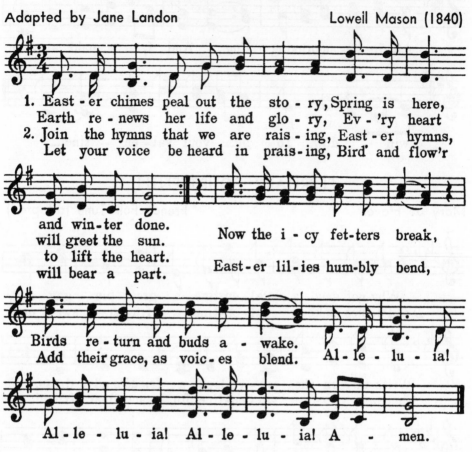

1. East - er chimes peal out the sto - ry, Spring is here,
   Earth re - news her life and glo - ry, Ev - 'ry heart
2. Join the hymns that we are rais - ing, East - er hymns,
   Let your voice be heard in prais - ing, Bird' and flow'r

and win - ter done.
will greet the sun.
to lift the heart.
will bear a part.

Now the i - cy fet - ters break,

East - er lil - ies hum - bly bend,

Birds re - turn and buds a - wake.
Add their grace, as voic - es blend. Al - le - lu - ia!

Al - le - lu - ia! Al - le - lu - ia! A - men.

RHYTHMICAL RAIN

J. L. V.

J. Lilian Vandevere

With a swing

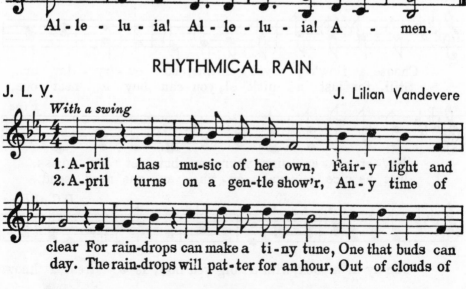

1. A - pril has mu - sic of her own, Fair - y light and
2. A - pril turns on a gen - tle show'r, An - y time of

clear For rain - drops can make a ti - ny tune, One that buds can
day. The rain - drops will pat - ter for an hour, Out of clouds of

hear. Lis-ten to the rain! (Drip - drop - drip - drop!) Oh,
grey. Lis-ten to the rain! (Drip - drop - drip - drop!) Oh,

lis-ten to the rain! (Drip - drop - drip - drop.) The cheer- y
lis-ten to the rain! (Drip - drop - drip - drop.) We know that

rob - in is glad for the tune, it helps him to sing.
sun-shine will soon come a-gain, so no one can pout.

Blos-soms hear it fall. (Drip-drop-drip-drop!) They ans-wer to the
Hear the stead-y beat, (Drip-drop-drip-drop!) That show-ers all re-

call. (Drip-drop-drip-drop!) The A- pril rain will fur nish
peat. (Drip-drop-drip-drop!) The A- pril rain is drum-ming

drum-beats For the gay pa - rade of spring.
gai - ly, And the buds come march-ing out.

SURE SIGNS

Clinton Cole

Stuart Bliss Hoppin

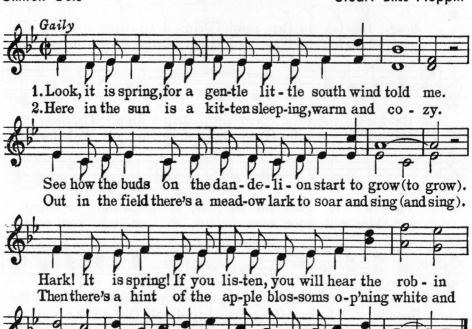

Gaily

1. Look, it is spring, for a gen-tle lit-tle south wind told me.
2. Here in the sun is a kit-ten sleep-ing, warm and co-zy.

See how the buds on the dan-de-li-on start to grow (to grow).
Out in the field there's a mead-ow lark to soar and sing (and sing).

Hark! It is spring! If you lis-ten, you will hear the rob-in
Then there's a hint of the ap-ple blos-soms o-p'ning white and

scold me, This is a day for fish-ing in a brook I know.
ros-y. So you can see I'm ab-so-lute-ly sure it's spring.

THE SPRING SOLOIST (Canon)

J. L. V.

J. Lilian Vandevere

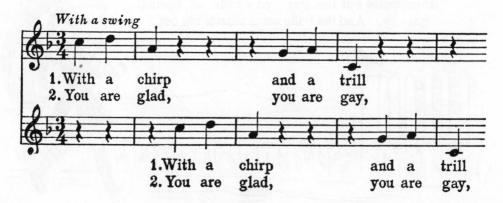

With a swing

1. With a chirp and a trill
2. You are glad, you are gay,

1. With a chirp and a trill
2. You are glad, you are gay,

Rob-in Red-breast will now ser-e-nade you.
'Tis the way that the rob-in has made you.

Rob-in Red-breast will now ser-e-nade
'Tis the way that the rob-in has made

With a lilt and a will
All at once it is May,

you. With a lilt and a will
you. All at once it is May,

He will broad-cast, an-nounc-ing the spring.
With a rob-in be-gin-ning to sing.

He will broad-cast the spring.
With a rob-in to sing.

SPEAKING OF SEASONS

Some like autumn weather, its days of blue and gold.
Some prefer the winter, with snow and sparkling cold.
Some are choosing summer, the sports long days will bring.
  They're welcome to,
  But when they do,
I'll take spring!

— *J. Lilian Vandevere*

THE HURDY-GURDY

Mary de Haven   Harvey Worthington Loomis

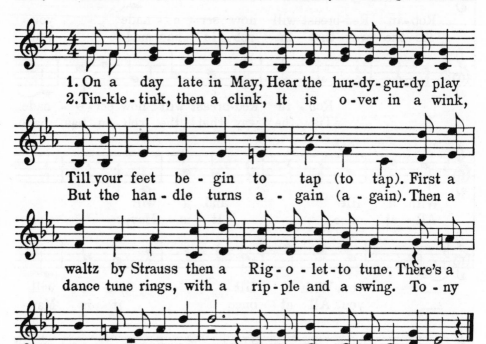

1. On a day late in May, Hear the hur-dy-gur-dy play
2. Tin-kle-tink, then a clink, It is o-ver in a wink,

Till your feet be-gin to tap (to tap). First a
But the han-dle turns a-gain (a-gain). Then a

waltz by Strauss then a Rig-o-let-to tune. There's a
dance tune rings, with a rip-ple and a swing. To-ny

tone that's a tri-fle flat, But who cares for a thing like that.
knows we will pay him well, When he comes with a tune to sell.

MIDSUMMER NIGHT

Frederick A. Winthrop   Robert Schumann

Moon-light falls o'er qui-et hill and val-ley, Song-birds
Shad-ows haunt the fra-grant jas-mine al-ley, Ghost-like

rest with-in the dream-y grove,
va-pors . . . . thro' the for-est rove.

THE PRETTY MAID MILKING HER COW

David Stevens   Irish Tune

1. It was on a bright morn-ing in sum-mer, When the
2. But at that I grew bold-er and bold-er, And I
3. So I'll make a short tale of a long one, And a

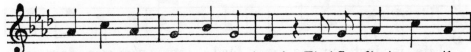

rob-in sang sweet on the bough, That I first saw the
said,"Will you mar-ry me now?" She re-plied,"What a
ver-y good plan,you'll al-low; In a month from that

eyes,blue as heav-en, Of the pret-ty maid milk-ing her
thing to be ask-ing Of a pret-ty maid milk-ing her
day I was wed-ded To the pret-ty maid milk-ing her

cow. Those eyes were turned a-way so de-mure-ly, With the
cow." Said I, "It is a bright sum-mer morn-ing, And the
cow. The years have been of sun-shine and shad-ow, Yet to

shad-ow of a frown on her brow, I feared that my
birds are sing-ing sweet on the bough,What time could be
all I will for-ev-er a-vow, I bless the bright

glance was un-wel-come To the pret-ty maid milk-ing her cow.
bet-ter for woo-ing Of a pret-ty maid milk-ing her cow?"
morn-ing that led me To the pret-ty maid milk-ing her cow.

171

SUMMERLAND

G. F. M.

George Frederick McKay

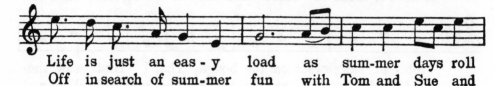

1. Whis-tling down a dust-y road be-neath a sum-mer sky.
2. Up to greet the morn-ing sun now smil-ing o'er the hill.

Life is just an eas-y load as sum-mer days roll
Off in search of sum-mer fun with Tom and Sue and

by. We'll sit and dream be-side a pleas-ant stream. We'll
Bill. We'll row our boat a-cross the qui-et lake. We'll

stroll a - long through the trees be-yond to a wood-land pond.
dream and wish as we troll in search of the sil - ver fish.

Whis-tling down a dust-y road past fields where I be - long.
Up to greet the morn-ing sun now smil - ing from the tree.

Joy - ful, sun-lit sum-mer-land, I love your hap-py song.
Blue, green, gold-en sum-mer-land, O lin - ger on with me.

If you like, after singing this song, whistle it all
the way through, or only the last four measures.

Tuneful Tim Broadcasts

RADIO MUSIC TALKS FOR BOYS AND GIRLS

GOOD MORNING, boys and girls. This is Tuneful Tim speaking. You will remember that you have sung many songs that you could play on the black keys of the piano,—songs in the *pentatonic* or *five-tone* scale:

This is a very old scale, and a great deal of folk music is written in it. Look at the songs on pages 20 and 36 for examples. You will notice that these tunes center around the home tone of the scale— *do* or *1*—and give us a bright or *major* feeling. Can you find other examples in the book?

Now look at *The Navajo Blanket* on page 112. Do you see that this tune centers around *la* or *6* and gives us a more sober, minor feeling?

This is especially true when a tune ends with $\overset{\text{la so la}}{\text{6 5 6}}$.

Sometimes you will find a tune that seems to be part *major* and part *minor*, such as *Barkalingo, Wahtermillion* on page 113.

The *pentatonic* scale is also sometimes called a *gapped* scale. Can you tell why it is given this name? Look closely to see what tones are left out of our *major* scale, which moves right along, step-wise, $\overset{\text{do re mi fa so la ti do}}{1\ 2\ 3\ 4\ 5\ 6\ 7\ 8}$. Pentatonic

Major	do	re	mi	fa	so	la	ti	do
	1	2	3	4	5	6	7	8
Pentatonic	do	re	mi		so	la		do
	1	2	3		5	6		8

Why not write some songs in the pentatonic scale?
Good-bye for this time!

G OOD MORNING again, boys and girls. Today we will talk about more scales.

There is a group of very old scales—hundreds and hundreds of years old — that began, long ago, in Greece. They grew, along with music, especially church music, and they are also found in folk songs. They are called *modes*, and you can easily find out how they sound. Our major scale, $\overset{\text{do re mi fa so la ti do}}{1\ 2\ 3\ 4\ 5\ 6\ 7\ 8}$, is one of them.

Now start on $\overset{\text{re}}{2}$ and sing up the tones of the scale to high $\overset{\text{re}}{2}$. It sounds rather queer, but nice, doesn't it? Now start on $\overset{\text{mi}}{3}$ and sing up to high $\overset{\text{mi}}{3}$. Then start on $\overset{\text{fa}}{4}$; then on $\overset{\text{so}}{5}$; on $\overset{\text{la}}{6}$; on $\overset{\text{ti}}{7}$ —and you have them all. Each one of them is a separate *mode* or scale.

If you play the piano, it is fun to find the *modes* there. Start first on C and play all the white keys up to the next C. Then start on D and play all the white keys up to the next D. Then play from E to E, from F to F and so on, always playing only the white keys, until you have reached C again for a starting note.

The *modes* which we find most often are the one built on $\overset{\text{la}}{6}$ (which is our *natural minor* scale) and the one built on $\overset{\text{re}}{2}$.

Here is a lovely church tune built on $\overset{\text{la}}{6}$:

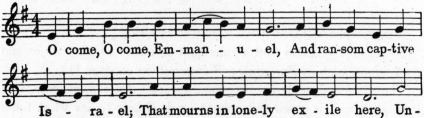

O come, O come, Em-man - u - el, And ran-som cap-tive
Is - ra - el; That mourns in lone-ly ex - ile here, Un-

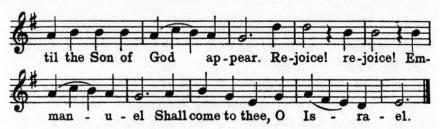

til the Son of God ap-pear. Re-joice! re-joice! Em-man-u-el Shall come to thee, O Is - ra - el.

Look at the song *A Friend in Need*, on page 72, for an example of a folk song in this same *mode*. Don't you like the $^{la\ so\ la}_{6\ \ 5\ \ 6}$ at the end of these tunes? Compare this with the $^{la\ si\ la}_{6\ \#5\ 6}$ at the end of *God Bless the Master of This House* on page 163. $^{La\ si\ la}_{6\ \#5\ 6}$ is the ending we hear more often today, and it comes from the *minor* scale that is made by raising *so* or *5* of the *natural minor* scale.

Here are two tunes built on *re* or *2*, the first one a folk tune, and the second one written by a living composer, Sidney Davidoff.

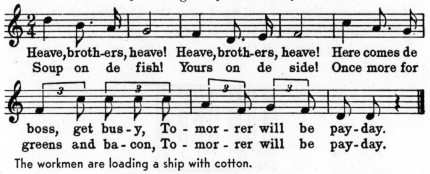

Heave, broth-ers, heave! Heave, broth-ers, heave! Here comes de
Soup on de fish! Yours on de side! Once more for

boss, get bus-y, To - mor - rer will be pay-day.
greens and ba-con, To - mor - rer will be pay-day.

The workmen are loading a ship with cotton.

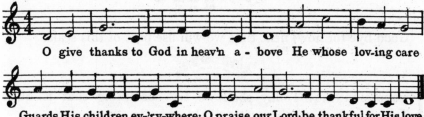

O give thanks to God in heav'n a - bove He whose lov-ing care

Guards His children ev-'ry-where; O praise our Lord; be thankful for His love.

Aren't they interesting tunes? You might look through the book and see how many examples of *modal la* or *6* tunes you can find. Then find as many *minor* tunes as you can that have $^{la\ si\ la}_{6\ \#5\ 6}$ or just $^{si\ la}_{\#5\ 6}$ in them.

Good-bye for this time.

Good morning! Would you like to try a scale that is quite new, compared to the *modes*, and one which is used a great deal in what we call *modern* music?

If so, see if you can do this:

Sing $\overset{\text{do re mi}}{1\ 2\ 3}$; then call $\overset{\text{mi}}{3}$ "$\overset{\text{"do"}}{1}$" and sing $\overset{\text{do re mi}}{1\ 2\ 3}$ again; call $\overset{\text{mi}}{3}$ "$\overset{\text{"do"}}{1}$" and sing $\overset{\text{do re mi}}{1\ 2\ 3}$ again. Call the last $\overset{\text{mi}}{3}$ "$\overset{\text{"do"}}{8}$" and sing high $\overset{\text{do}}{8}$, then low $\overset{\text{do}}{1}$. You will find, if you have sung correctly, that the low $\overset{\text{do}}{1}$ is the $\overset{\text{do}}{1}$ where you started. This is really just a *sequence* of $\overset{\text{do re mis}}{1\ 2\ 3s}$.

Now can you *think* the $\overset{\text{do re mis}}{1\ 2\ 3s}$ and *sing* them with *loo* or *ah?*

This is difficult, but I think you can do it—try to *think* the change quickly while you sing, with *loo* or *ah*, like this:

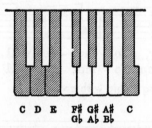

If you can do this you will have sung the *whole tone* scale, which you hear quite often in the music of today.

If you wish to play it on the piano, play the keys that are colored gray in this picture.

Good-bye for now; next time we will use part of this scale.

Good morning! Today shall we try something that is quite modern? Let's sing, with syllables or *Ah:*

Now

and

then

You will see that these are just little fragments or *figures* from the downward-moving whole tone scale. Boys, do you think you can sing them as an alto part, like this?—

Let's try a tune using some of these figures:

Doesn't it sound like some of the music you hear over the radio? Now can you syncopate it?

Which rhythm do you like better? Can you write words that will suit both rhythms?

Good-bye for this time!

GOOD MORNING again! Soon you will be singing three-part music. You have already sung three-part rounds and some two-part songs with descants as third parts. Here are some three-part harmonies. Can you sing them, making your part blend nicely with the other two?

Good-bye, boys and girls. May you have a lot of fun with your three-part singing. And don't forget to make more and better songs of your own.

Tuneful Tim signing off!

For the School Glee Club

*"Since singing is so good a thing,
I wish all men would learn to sing."*

— *William Byrd (1542-1623)*

I KNOW A BANK

Shakespeare (abridged)   Charles E. Horn (abridged)

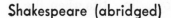

1. I know a bank where-on the wild thyme grows,
2. I know a bank where-on the wild thyme grows,

I know a bank where-on the wild thyme grows, Where
With sweet musk ros - es and with eg - lan - tine; There

ox - slips and the nod-ding vio-let blows, Where ox-slips
sleeps Ti - ta - nia some-time of the night, Lulled in these

and the nod-ding vio-let blows; I know a bank where-
flow'rs with danc- es and de-light; I know a bank where-

on the wild thyme grows,— the wild thyme grows.
on the wild thyme grows,— the wild thyme grows.

IN THE WOODS

F. Korner
English adaptation by Stephen Fay

Robert Franz

Gracefully, not too slowly

The woods, the woods are fresh and green, The shad-ows lie

soft - ly with flow'rs be-tween. There is joy— in life when the

day is new. When the sun shines bright and the sky is

blue In wood-lands, shad - y wood - lands.

When, red thro' the branch-es, the eve-ning sun Pro-

claims to all that the day is done, Home-ward we

go with lag-ging feet, En - chant - ed still by the

charm so sweet Of wood-lands, shad - y wood - lands.

WHEN TWILIGHT FALLS

J. Lilian Vandevere

Josephine Knowles Kendel

West-ern skies are soft-ly glow-ing, There the eve-ning
D.C. Gone is all the sun-set gleam-ing, Twi-light is the

star is show-ing, Through the dusk a night bird calls.
time for dream-ing, Through the blue the moon will rise.

Leave the cares of day be-hind you, Let the spell of
Then, al-though no word is spo-ken, Twi-light's love-ly

fire-light bind you, Rest a-while, as twi-light
spell is bro-ken, Night has come and fire-light

falls. Set the logs to blaz-ing
dies. Hm

bright-ly, Set the flames to leap-ing high.

Let them glow and flick-er light-ly, While the shad-ows fill the sky.

OVER THE BRIGHT BLUE SEA

W. S. Gilbert

Arthur S. Sullivan
(in *H.M.S. Pinafore*)

With motion

O - ver the bright blue sea Comes Sir Jos - eph Por-ter,

K. C. B., Wher - ev - er he may go,—

Bang! bang! the loud nine-pound-ers go; Shout o'er the bright blue

sea— For Sir Jos-eph Por-ter, K. C. B.

Shout o'er the bright blue sea— For Sir Jos-eph Por-ter, K. C.

B., For Sir Jos-eph Por-ter, K. C. B.

PAESANELLO

Translated by Helen C. Dykema   Italian Popular Song

In a val-ley 'neath a moun-tain, *Pa -**e - sa - nel-lo,—

Close be-side a spar-kling foun-tain, Pa - e - sa-nel- lo,—

There I saw a love-ly maid- en,— Pa - e - sa-nel- lo,—

Laugh-ing and sing-ing this gay lit-tle song, Pa - e - sa-

nel - lo.— Tra - la - la, tra - la - la, Tra

la - la - la - la, Lit - tle pop- py,— lit - tle

flow - er,— Tra - la - la, tra - la - la, tra-

la - la - la - la, scar-let pop-py,— fair-est flow- er.—

*Pa (pronounce "a" as "o" in pop). **E (pronounce "e" as "ay" in hay).

A SONG OF SUNSHINE

Gwen Rowland   Peter W. Dykema

O ROBIN, COME

Helen Call

Mary Root Kern

1. O rob-in, come and sing your song, The
puss-y wil-lows are show-ing. The day-light now is
clear and long, And A-pril her bu-gle is blow-ing. The
ma-ple spray with red is gay, The wil-low a sun-ny
yel-low. So rob-in a-wing, Fly here and sing Your
song so joy-ful and mel-low.

2. The brooks are danc-ing down the hill, And
green is o-ver the mead-ow. The fields, a-stir from
win-t'ry chill, Lie dap-pled with sun and shad-ow. The
lit-tle lamb-kins leap and spring, For gone is the win-ter
sor-row. We wel-come the spring, So come and sing To
bid the world good-mor-row.

WHERE'ER YOU WALK

William Congreve   George Frederick Handel*

Wher-e'er you walk, cool gales shall fan the glade, Trees, where you sit, shall crowd in-to a shade, Trees, where you sit, shall crowd in-to a shade; Wher-e'er you walk, cool gales shall fan the glade, Trees, where you sit, shall crowd in-to a shade, in-to a shade, in-to a shade, Trees, where you sit, shall crowd in-to a shade.

Wher-e'er you tread, the blush-ing flow'rs shall rise, And all things flour-ish, and all things flour-ish, Wher-e'er you turn your eyes, Wher-e'er you turn your eyes, Wher-e'er you turn your eyes.

*To make the song easier to read, the liberty has been taken of changing the time signature and notation to correspond. **The rests may be omitted when the accompaniment is not used.

O'ER THE HILLS AWAY

Paul Hastings

Dr. Thomas Arne

Brightly

1. Come out, come out and breathe the air, And
2. Come out, come out and greet the flow'rs, The
3. Come out, come out, the road is free, For

live the glo - rious day!__ The wind is sweet, the
bloom is on the may;__ The blos - soms of the
who shall say us nay?__ The world was made for

skies are fair, The wind is sweet, the skies are fair, Come
field are ours, The blos - soms of the field are ours, Come
you and me, The world was made for you and me, Come

Fine

out and o'er the hills a - way, We'll o'er the hills a - way!__
out and o'er the hills a - way, We'll o'er the hills a - way!__
out and o'er the hills a - way, We'll o'er the hills a - way!__

D.S. al Fine

We'll o'er the hills a - way; We'll o'er the hills a - way; Come

THE HAND-ORGAN MAN

Translated by J. L. V.

Franz Peter Schubert

The organ plays eight measures. (Omit rest if accompaniment is not used.) (The organ)

Rather slowly

1. Near the lit-tle vil-lage stands an or-gan man,
2. No one stops or lis-tens when his mu-sic peals.

There, with numb-ing fin-gers play-ing as he can.
Dogs are growl-ing cross-ly near the old man's heels.

Bare-foot in the win-ter he must ev-er stray.
Ev-'ry-thing a-bout him goes the way it will,

See his plate for pen-nies, emp-ty ev-'ry day.
While he keeps on turn-ing, old songs ech-o still.

See his plate for pen-nies, emp-ty ev-'ry day.
While he keeps on turn-ing, old songs ech-o still.

Or-gan grind-er, tell me, Shall I go your way?

Might your tin-kling or-gan learn my song, to play?

AMERICA, THE BEAUTIFUL

Katharine Lee Bates

Samuel A. Ward

1. O beau-ti-ful for spa-cious skies, For am-ber waves of grain, For pur-ple moun-tain
2. O beau-ti-ful for pil-grim feet, Whose stern im-pas-sioned stress A thor-ough-fare for
3. O beau-ti-ful for he-roes proved In lib-er-at-ing strife, Who more than self their
4. O beau-ti-ful for pa-triot dream That sees be-yond the years Thine al-a-bas-ter

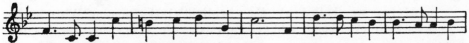

maj-es-ties A-bove the fruit-ed plain. A-mer-i-ca! A-mer-i-ca! God
free-dom beat A-cross the wil-der-ness. A-mer-i-ca! A-mer-i-ca! God
Coun-try loved, And mer-cy more than life. A-mer-i-ca! A-mer-i-ca! May
cit-ies gleam Un-dimmed by hu-man tears. A-mer-i-ca! A-mer-i-ca! God

shed His grace on thee, And crown thy good with broth-er-hood From sea to shin-ing sea!
mend thine ev-'ry flaw, Con-firm thy soul in self-con-trol, Thy lib-er-ty in law.
God thy gold re-fine Till all suc-cess be no-ble-ness And ev-'ry gain di-vine.
shed His grace on thee, And crown thy good with broth-er-hood From sea to shin-ing sea!

AMERICA

S. F. Smith

Henry Carey (?)

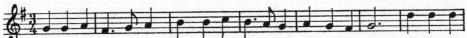

1. My coun-try, 'tis of thee, Sweet land of lib-er-ty, Of thee I sing. Land where my
2. My na-tive coun-try thee, Land of the no-ble free, Thy name I love. I love thy
3. Let mu-sic swell the breeze, And ring from all the trees Sweet freedom's song. Let mor-tal
4. Our fa-thers' God, to Thee, Au-thor of lib-er-ty, To Thee we sing. Long may our

fa-thers died! Land of the Pilgrim's pride! From ev-'ry moun-tain side, Let freedom ring!
rocks and rills, Thy woods and templed hills; My heart with rap-ture thrills Like that a-bove.
tongues awake; Let all that breathe par-take; Let rocks their si-lence break, The sound prolong.
land be bright With freedom's ho-ly light; Protect us by Thy might, Great God, our King!

189

THE STAR-SPANGLED BANNER

Francis Scott Key

John Stafford Smith

O say! can you see by the dawn's ear-ly light, What so
O thus be it ev-er, when free-men shall stand Be-

proud-ly we hailed at the twi-light's last gleam-ing? Whose broad
tween their loved home and grim war's des-o-la-tion! Blest with

stripes and bright stars, thro' the per-il-ous fight, O'er the
vic-t'ry and peace, may the heav'n-res-cued land Praise the

ram-parts we watched, were so gal-lant-ly stream-ing? And the
Pow'r that has made and pre-served us a na-tion! Then

rock-et's red glare, The bombs burst-ing in air Gave
con-quer we must, For our cause it is just, And

proof thro' the night that our flag was still there.
this be our mot-to, "In God is our trust!"

O say, does that Star-Span-gled Ban-ner yet
And the Star-Span-gled Ban-ner in tri-umph shall

wave O'er the land of the free and the home of the brave!

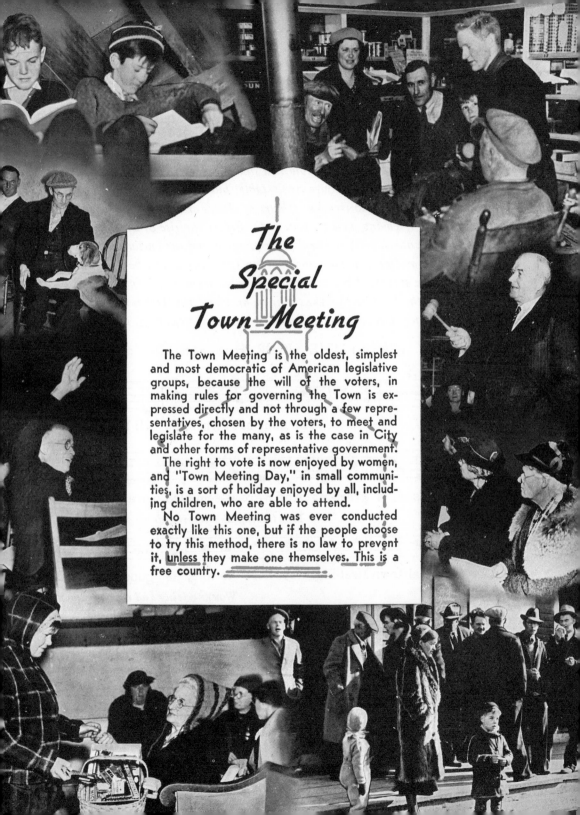

The Special Town Meeting

The Town Meeting is the oldest, simplest and most democratic of American legislative groups, because the will of the voters, in making rules for governing the Town is expressed directly and not through a few representatives, chosen by the voters, to meet and legislate for the many, as is the case in City and other forms of representative government.

The right to vote is now enjoyed by women, and "Town Meeting Day," in small communities, is a sort of holiday enjoyed by all, including children, who are able to attend.

No Town Meeting was ever conducted exactly like this one, but if the people choose to try this method, there is no law to prevent it, unless they make one themselves. This is a free country.

THE SPECIAL TOWN MEETING

An Operetta in One Act

Libretto by David Stevens   *Music by* Gladys Pitcher

SCENE: *The Assembly Room of the Town Hall, a table for the* MODER-
ATOR *on a raised platform. Below is a small table for the* TOWN CLERK.
A chair at R. near the MODERATOR'S *table, but below on the floor is a
chair for the* TOWN CONSTABLE. *Chairs or settees are placed on each side
for the voters, leaving a clear space at C. Before the rise of the curtain a
bell (like a church bell) is heard for a moment and the curtain rises and
discloses an assembly of men and women (as many as can be accommo
dated on the stage). They are seated in equal numbers, men on the R.,
women on the L. The* MODERATOR *is in his chair, the* TOWN CLERK *and*
CONSTABLE *are in their places. The* CHORUS OF VOTERS *sing, seated:*

(*Chorus*) THE HOUR HAS STRUCK

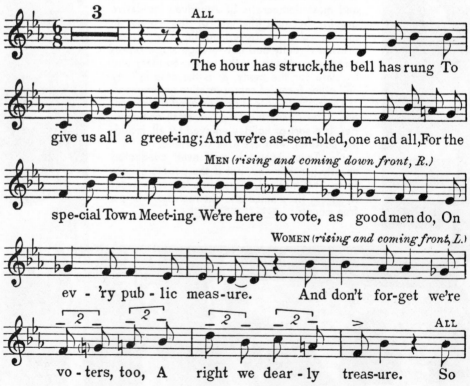

The hour has struck, the bell has rung To
give us all a greet-ing; And we're as-sem-bled, one and all, For the
spe-cial Town Meet-ing. We're here to vote, as good men do, On
ev - 'ry pub - lic meas-ure. And don't for-get we're
vo - ters, too, A right we dear - ly treas-ure. So

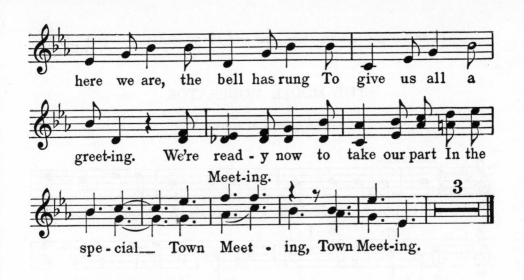

here we are, the bell has rung To give us all a greet-ing. We're read-y now to take our part In the Meet-ing. spe-cial__ Town Meet-ing, Town Meet-ing.

MODERATOR (*pounding with his gavel*) The meeting will please come to order!

THE MODEL MODERATOR

(Moderator and Chorus)

MODERATOR

I'll now pro-claim How I be-came A Mod-el Mod-er-

a-tor.__

%1

1. When I was a young-ster I
2. If an-y of you have a

used to at-tend All meet-ings like this we are
mo-tion to make, Re-mem-ber it al-ways is

hold-ing; Neg-lect-ed my chores and my
reck-oned A ver-y good plan to be

stud-ies as well, For which I got man-y a
sure that you have A quick and re-li-a-ble

scold-ing. But still I would go ev-'ry
sec-ond. And then you must wait till you

chance I got, Re-gard-less of stud-ies and
catch my eye, I rec-og-nize you with a

schools, And that is the way I be-came ex-pert In the
smile,— And then you pro-ceed to de-bate the point In a

Par-lia-men-ta-ry Rules. So— Now I sit in the
Par-lia-men-ta-ry Style.

Mod-er-a-tor's chair, A gav-el in my hand and with

dig-ni-ty to spare. I was law-ful-ly e-

lect-ed And my rules must be re-spect-ed, I'm a

Mod-el Mod-er-a-tor of a kind that's get-ting rare.

f ALL
He was law-ful-ly e-lect-ed And his rules must be re-

spect-ed, He's a Mod-el Mod-er-a-tor of a

1st Verse
kind that's get-ting rare.

D.S.

2nd Verse
kind that's get-ting rare.

5

(*The* CHORUS *repeats the last three lines of the refrain as before.*)

Mod.	(*at close of song*) We will now proceed to the business of the meeting. You all know that we have been called together to see if the voters will authorize the building of a new school house.

(*All the* Voters *rise and wave their arms wildly.*)

Chorus	(*all shouting*) Mr. Moderator!
Mod.	(*pounding with his gavel*) Stop!
Constable	(*blowing police whistle and holding up his hand*) Stop!
Mod.	(*to* Constable) Thanks, Mr. Constable, but there is nothing in the Parliamentary Rules about whistles.
Con.	(*putting whistle in his vest pocket*) O.K., Mr. Moderator.
Mod.	Only one of you caught my eye. I recognize our genial fellow-townsman and proprietor of the general store, Amos Tinker.
Amos	(*rising*) Mr. Moderator, it seems to me that before we vote on this school house matter, we ought to consider where it is to be located. Now, there's a couple of acres of level ground right next to my store, and it's for sale.
Caleb	(*speaking from his seat*) Who owns it?
Mod.	(*rapping*) Order, please!
Amos	Well, I do, and you know it. So what?
Mod.	(*rapping*) Order!
Amos	That's the place for the school house and I'll tell you why. (*Sings:*)

196

THE GENERAL STORE

(Amos and Chorus)

AMOS

In my gen-er-al store I keep an am-ple stock Of slates and rul-ers and e-ras-ers and chalk, With pen-cils, pens and pa-per and such, All read-y for the scho-lars, and they don't cost much; A-rith-me-tic, gram-mar and spell-in' books, too, Mc Guf-fey's First Read-ers, sec-ond hand or new, Pi-an-o ex-er-cis-es that show you how to play, And an up-to-date At-las of the U. S. A. And that's the rea-son, I think you'll a-gree, For buy-ing that two a-cre lot, you see I'd rath-er not sell it, But

if you com-pel it, I'll make the price right if you leave it to me.

ALL

If we let him tell it, He'd rath-er not sell it, But

he nev-er thinks of him - self, not he!__

(AMOS *takes his seat, much pleased with himself.*)

VOTERS   (*all rising except* AMOS) Mr. Moderator!

MOD.   Caleb caught my eye that time. He has the floor. (*All sit except* CALEB.)

CALEB   Mr. Moderator, it seems to me that Amos is a leetle bit selfish — just a leetle. Now you all know that I have a candy store at the other end of town and there's a vacant lot right next to me.

AMOS   Who owns it?

CALEB   (*rather confused*) Well-er — I do, of course; but that ain't the point. The point is that the kids can come right into my place at recess and after school. That's the place for the new school, and I'll tell you the reason why. (*Sings:*)

THE CANDY STORE

(*Caleb and Chorus*)

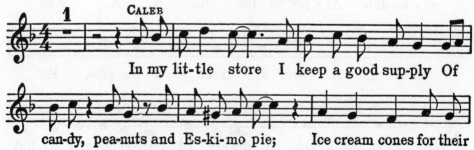

In my lit-tle store I keep a good sup-ply Of

can-dy, pea-nuts and Es-ki-mo pie; Ice cream cones for their

nick-els and their dimes, And all day suck-ers and a
tub of pick-led limes. Lic-'rice sticks and dou-ble-mint gum,
Han-dy by when the kid-dies come. And if they hap-pen to
o-ver-eat, There's a doc-tor's of-fice right a-cross the street. So
that's the rea-son it's best to buy That strip of land, and the
cost is-n't high. A two a-cre slice I'll sell at a price;
It's the place for the school, and I've told you why.

ALL

He'll sell at a price that two a-cre slice, He's a
lib-er-al chap, and we all___ know why.___

(CALEB *resumes his seat.*)

199

AMOS	(*rising*) Mr. Moderator.
MOD.	Mr. Tinker.
AMOS	I move ye that the chair appoint a committee of three to negotiate for the purchase of that two-acre place next to my store.
MOD.	You hear the motion. Is it seconded? (*Silence*)
CONSTABLE	(*rising*) Well, I'll second it if nobody else wants to. Jest to get a vote.
MOD.	It is moved and seconded et cetera. All those in favor will say "Aye."
AMOS	Aye!
MOD.	All opposed will say "No."

(*All, except* AMOS, *rise and shout vociferously.*)

VOTERS	NO!!!
MOD.	The motion is lost. (*pounds with his gavel*)
CALEB	Mr. Moderator.
MOD.	Mr. Plunket.
CALEB	I move ye, sir, that the chair appoint a committee of three to negotiate for the purchase of that slice of land next to my store.
MOD.	You hear the motion. Is it seconded? (*Silence*)
CLERK	(*rising*) Well, I hain't had anything to say, so far, I'll second it.
MOD.	It is moved and seconded, et cetera. All those in favor will say "Aye."
CALEB	(*feebly*) Aye.
MOD.	Those opposed will say "No."
VOTERS	(*as before, except* CALEB) NO!!!
MOD.	The motion is lost. (*Bang gavel*)
NANCY	(*rising*) Mr. Moderator.
MOD.	Miss Wick.
NANCY	You all know that I'm the school teacher, and I think I know where the school should be located. We seem to have forgotten that the town owns a piece of land about half way between the two sites that have been mentioned.
AMOS	(*interrupting*) That's it! Women meddlin'!
CALEB	Ye're right, Amos.

MOD.	(*banging with his gavel*) Order! Order! Proceed, Nancy.
NANCY	I move, sir, that we take a recess of an hour, and re-assemble to consider an appropriation for building a new school house on the town property.
ALL	(*except* AMOS *and* CALEB) I second the motion.
MOD.	You have heard the motion and — er — I think it was seconded. Are you ready for the question?
AMOS AND CALEB	NO!
ALL THE OTHER VOTERS	Yes, Yes!
MOD.	All in favor will say "Aye."
ALL	(*except* AMOS *and* CALEB) Aye!!
MOD.	Those opposed will say "No."

(AMOS *and* CALEB *say nothing, but shake their heads slowly.*)

CONSTABLE	(*to* AMOS *and* CALEB) Come on, come on, say "No."
AMOS	(*disgusted*) What's the use?
CALEB	Ye're right, Amos, we're a hopeless minority.
MOD.	The motion is carried and the meeting will take a recess of an hour and re-assemble in accordance to Miss Wick's motion. (*Bangs with his gavel*)

A RECESS, THOUGH BRIEF

A re-cess, though brief, Is a great re-lief, We have had a rath-er storm-y ses-sion; But ma-jor-i-ties rule, And we're going to have a school On land in the town's pos-ses-sion. A-mos, we're sor-ry, Ca-leb, don't wor-ry, You will find that it's bet-ter our way. We are all friends here, And we nev-er need to fear When the voice of the man-y we o - bey, o - bey! When the voice of the man-y we_ o - bey!_

THE PLAY ENDS

Jeannette—Isabella

This song-play is from an old French carol. Jeannette and Isabella are two of the peasants who come to the stable, with torches and cakes, to see the new-born Babe. They come with joy, celebrate with a small feast, and return, quietly, the way they came. You might like to write a short introduction for a Narrator who will tell all this to your audience.

You may give the play by daylight, or with dim light, growing brighter when the peasants with torches arrive. For torches you may use brown paper cones at the end of sticks, filled with crushed orange crepe paper, and with streamers falling over the edges.

On the stage you may use three dark screens. Place lambs, cut from cardboard, against the left screen; against the right screen, a crude bench or table; and against the center screen, a low box, with a flash light on the bottom, for the manger, with a stool back of it for Mary. School clothes are good for the children; colored neck and head scarves for the boy and girl peasants. Some carry canes and some cakes. Mary should have a veil of old rose or grey-blue over her head and shoulders; Joseph, a neckerchief, and a staff to carry.

You may have other ideas for presenting the play, but, whatever you do, it should be performed in a spirit of reverent joy.

JEANNETTE-ISABELLA

A Christmas Song-Play

Translation by BERTA ELSMITH   *Arranged around an old French Carol*
by BERTA ELSMITH

Music adapted by GLADYS PITCHER

PRELUDE

The curtains are closed. Two groups of CHILDREN *are in front of the stage, right and left. One* CHILD *and the* PEASANTS *are back of the audience, ready to come down the center aisle. (Instead of a curtain a screen may be placed before the manger, to be removed by two* CHILDREN *at the Introduction.)*

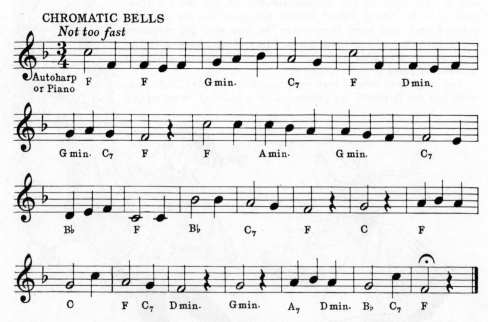

Music I — INTRODUCTION

The curtains part slowly, showing MARY *and* JOSEPH *behind the manger. The light is dim.*

BELLS   Old French Carol

A CHILD *comes down the center aisle, looking at* MARY, *goes part way up steps and pauses, then runs to the right of the stage, and joins other* CHILDREN. *They join* CHILDREN *from the left at center of stage, whisper,*

and point up, and gather beside the stairs to the stage.

Music II — TORCHES HERE

CHILDREN *(beckoning to back of hall)* Some PEASANTS *with lighted torches*

Not too fast

Autoharp or Piano

Torch-es here, Jean-nette Is-a-bel-la! Torch-es here, to His

G   G   A min.   D₇   G   G

come quietly through the audience, and join CHILDREN *at steps.*

JOSEPH *and* MARY

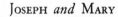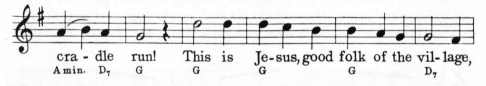

cra-dle run! This is Je-sus, good folk of the vil-lage,

A min. D₇ G   G   G   G   D₇

ALL *(They look up, admiring*

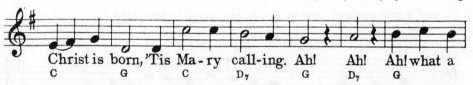

Christ is born, 'Tis Ma-ry call-ing. Ah! Ah! Ah! what a

C   G   C   D₇   G   D₇   G

the scene in the stable, and nod to each other with joy.)

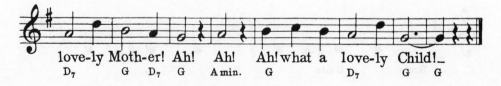

love-ly Moth-er! Ah! Ah! Ah! what a love-ly Child!_

D₇   G D₇ G   A min.   G   D₇   G G

Several CHILDREN and PEASANTS tiptoe up steps to manger and look at the BABY, then to front of stage and beckon to friends below. ALL sing softly, audience joining.

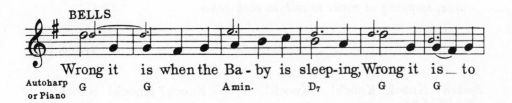

BELLS

Wrong it is when the Ba-by is sleep-ing, Wrong it is__ to

Autoharp G   G   A min.   D₇   G   G
or Piano

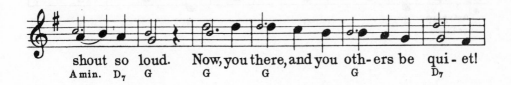

shout so loud.   Now, you there, and you oth-ers be qui-et!

A min. D₇ G   G   G   G   D₇

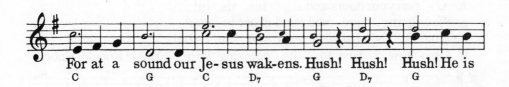

For at a   sound our Je-sus wak-ens. Hush! Hush! Hush! He is

C   G   C   D₇   G   D₇   G

sleep-ing sound-ly, Hush! Hush! Hush! do but see Him sleep!__

D₇   G D₇ G A min. E₇ A min. D₇   G

MUSIC III — WHO KNOCKS?

Some PEASANTS at the back of the hall knock with their canes on the "knocks." Murmur of voices is heard through the music as some PEASANTS and WOMEN with plates of cakes walk down the center aisle, stopping at times to talk to each other.

French Tune

*Several people say each sentence, talking all at once, slowly, in the rhythm of the music.

208

Tra la la la la la la la! Tra la la la la la la la la!
G   G   C   G   G   G   A min. D₇

Tra la la la la la la la! Tra la la la la la la!
G   G   C   G   G   G   C A min. D₇

Spoken Knock! Knock! Knock! *(with canes, as before)* Knock! Knock! Knock!

BELLS

G   G   G   G

A. O - pen your doors and __ let us in! __
B. We bring __ joy and good cheer to you! __
C. Come, let us has - ten and see the Babe!
D. Oh, how __ fine to be com-ing here! Knock! Knock! Knock!

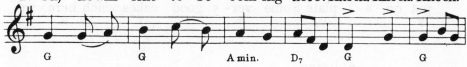

G   G   A min.   D₇   G   G

A. Oh, what joy to be com - ing here!
B. Wel-come, wel-come the love - ly Child!
C. Ah, how love-ly are Moth-er and Child!
Knock! Knock! Knock! D. Ah, how love-ly are Moth-er and Child!

G   G   G   D₇   G C   A min.   D₇   G

209

Music IV — WHO COMES THERE?

Joseph comes to head of stairs, arms out in a welcoming gesture. Those on stage gather around him. Joseph and those on stage sing.

The Carol

BELLS

Autoharp or Piano
G G⁹ G G C C C C₇

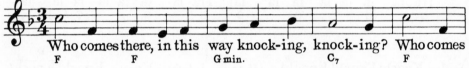

Who comes there, in this way knock-ing, knock-ing? Who comes
F F Gmin. C₇ F

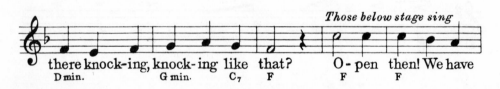

Those below stage sing

there knock-ing, knock-ing like that? O-pen then! We have
Dmin. Gmin. C₇ F F F

put on a plate Some ver-y good cakes,which here we
F C₇ B♭ F B♭

ALL *sing*

car-ry. Toc! Toc! Toc! O-pen wide the door then,
C₇ F C F C F C₇

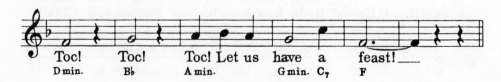

Toc! Toc! Toc! Let us have a feast!
Dmin. B♭ Amin. Gmin. C₇ F

210

Music V — DELIGHT OVER THE BABY

CHILDREN *sit on floor of stage, right and left; center of stage clear. Procession of* PEASANTS *and* WOMEN, *with canes and cakes, walks to stage. They curtsey to* MARY *and* JOSEPH, *and go slowly around to back of stage.*

French Tune

ALL *sing, forming a group around*

the manger, and show delight over the BABY. MARY *shows the* BABY *a cake. Those near show by pleased expression that He smiles. A* CHILD

peeps in manger, claps hands and jumps up and down. ALL *smile.* MARY *plays with* BABY (*who is never seen*) *to make Him smile.*

A small group of the best voices, PEASANTS, WOMEN and CHILDREN
remains on stage, or they come up from below the stage, greeting all

others as they go down the stairs to below stage.

Music VI — THE FEAST

ALL *sing, audience joining.* PEASANTS *on stage pass two plates of cakes to two* WOMEN *below stage. They pass the cakes slowly to* PEASANTS *there, who make gestures of taking cakes, bowing polite thanks, and pass back and forth, greeting each other and gathering in small groups. On stage three* WOMEN *pass cakes. The* CHILDREN, *sitting in a circle are the only ones who take cakes. No eating — the effect is that of a feast of love, and the movements suggest a ceremonial dance.* JOSEPH *and* MARY *look on with pleasure.*

Ah! Tra la la la la la la la la! Ah! Tra la la la
la la la la! O-pen then! We have put on a plate Some
ver-y good cakes, which here we car-ry. Tra! La!

As song draws to a close all movement stops. Those on stage move behind MARY *and* JOSEPH, CHILDREN *to right and left of stage. Those below form picture either side of stairs. Everything is still.*

Tra la la la! Tra la la! Tra! La! La! Let us
have a feast!

take torches and, as they sing, go softly down steps, through audience, and out at back, as the stage becomes dimly lit. Only the light from

the manger is on MARY's *face. All those below the stage curtsey toward*
MARY *and* JOSEPH, *and follow the others out.*

MUSIC VIII — ENDING

ALL *humming.   The* CHILDREN *go softly down the steps and follow
the others. The first* CHILD *lingers, stopping half-way down steps.*
MARY *waves to him; he waves his hand and goes out quietly, often*

looking back. MARY *waves him out of sight.*

All is quiet. MARY *and* JOSEPH *look down at the sleeping* JESUS. *The
curtains close slowly, or two* CHILDREN *may bring in the screen and
place it before the manger.*

THE PLAY ENDS

Hanukah
Its Significance

HANUKAH, an eight day festival celebrated by Jews for over two thousand years, commemorates the victory of a small group of Jews under the leadership of Judah Maccabeus for religious freedom and the re-dedication of the Temple at Jerusalem to the service of God (165 B.C.). Thus, Hanukah is known as the Feast of Dedication.

Before the Menorah

The big event on Hanukah is the candle-lighting ceremony, *Before the Menorah* (a special candelabra), with the lighting of a single candle the first evening and the number increasing by one each evening until, on the last night, the full eight candles are kindled. Thus, Hanukah is also known as the Feast of Lights.

Rock of Ages

On each of the eight days of the holiday, after the offering of the prayer of thanks to God for His Miracles and loving-kindness, which is part of the Menorah ceremony, the traditional hymn, *Rock of Ages* (*Ma-oz Tsur*) is sung in both home and synagogue.

My Dreydl

Hanukah is also a happy festival when gifts are given to the children, and family and community gatherings are held. At these, games are played, one of which is known as Dreydl — a sort of put-and-take game — which is played with a spinning top.

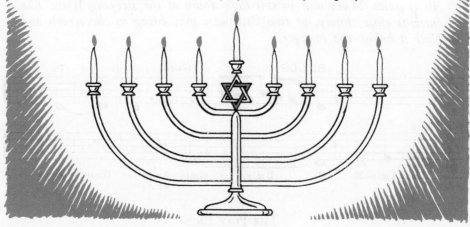

Before the Menorah

Elma Erlich Levinger

A. W. Bender

In the can-dle's rays I see
Sol - diers all, they smiled in pride,

Love-ly pic-tures beck-'ning me! Ju-dah with his
Glad and un - a - fraid they died. God of Is - rael,

Fine

shield and sword,— Pledged to bat-tle for the Lord;
may I be A sol - dier wor-thy them and Thee.

El - e - a - zar, stead-fast, strong, 'Mid the mock-ing

heath - en___ throng; Han - nah, straight as

D. C. al Fine

can - dle's flame, Sons who glo - ri - fied her name.

Used by permission of the Central Conference of American Rabbis.

Rock of Ages

M. Jastrow G. Gottlieb

Old Synagogal Melody

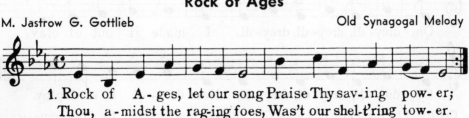

1. Rock of A - ges, let our song Praise Thy sav-ing pow- er;
Thou, a - midst the rag-ing foes, Was't our shel-t'ring tow- er.

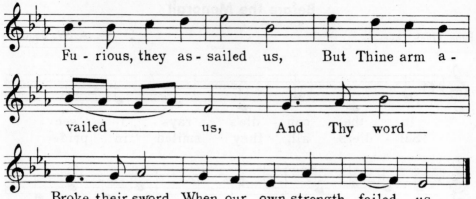

Fu - rious, they as - sailed us, But Thine arm a-
vailed _____ us, And Thy word _____
Broke their sword When our own strength failed _ us.

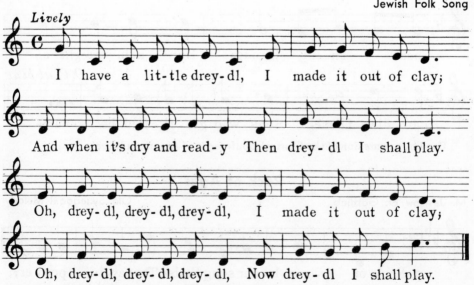

My Dreydl

Jewish Folk Song

Lively

I have a lit - tle drey - dl, I made it out of clay;

And when it's dry and read - y Then drey - dl I shall play.

Oh, drey - dl, drey - dl, drey - dl, I made it out of clay;

Oh, drey - dl, drey - dl, drey - dl, Now drey - dl I shall play.

218

ACKNOWLEDGMENTS

We wish to thank the magazine, *Story Parade,* for permission to use the poem, "America Sings"; Mrs. Lillian Mohr Fox, Supervisor of Music, Pasadena, California, for "Covered Wagon Days"; the magazine, *Child Life,* and the authors for the poems, "Pacific," "A Child's Prayer" and "Song of the Workers"; the Federal Works Agency, Work Projects Administration and the New Mexico Music Project for "At the Gate of Heaven"; John Lomax and The Macmillan Company for "The Rattle Sna-wa-wake" and "All the Pretty Little Horses" from *American Ballads and Folk Songs;* Mrs. Gerald A. Waring for the song "Margarida" collected by her; and The Cooperative Recreation Service of Delaware, Ohio for "Sweetheart Out A-Hunting." The words of "A Song of Sunshine," page 184, appeared in *The Christian Science Monitor* and are reprinted by permission. We thank Mr. Joseph H. Soifer and Dr. M. Delott Garber for the introduction to "Hanukah."

We wish also to thank Martha Powell Setchell for designing our book, for making the rhythm pictures, the photomontages and many of the illustrations; and Adelaide True Kelley and Esther Boston Bristol for many other illustrations.

For the use of the pictures in the photomontage on page 191, we wish to thank Mr. John Gould, author, and the Stephen Daye Press, publishers of *"New England Town Meeting."*

For the pictures used in the photomontages on pages 4, 83 and 153 we make the following acknowledgments:

Page 4:
1. New York skyline (*Keystone View Co.*)
2. Young tool and die worker (*Acme Photo*)
3. Power plant (*Keystone View Co.*)
4. Farmer (*Harold M. Lambert*)
5. Capitol at Washington, D. C. (*Philip D. Gendreau*)
6. American family (*Harold M. Lambert*)
7. Independence Hall, Philadelphia (*Philip D. Gendreau*)
8. Business man (*Harold M. Lambert*)

Page 83:
1. Statue of Liberty (*Harold M. Lambert*)
2. Mt. Rainier, Washington (*H. Armstrong Roberts*)
3. Hikers at Rainier National Park (*Philip D. Gendreau*)
4. Harvesting corn (*H. Armstrong Roberts*)
5. Hay makers (*Harold M. Lambert*)
6. Motoring, State of Washington (*H. Armstrong Roberts*)
7. Harvesting wheat (*Harold M. Lambert*)

Page 153:
1. Spring (*H. Armstrong Roberts*)
2. Summer (*H. Armstrong Roberts*)
3. Harvest (*Harold M. Lambert*)
4. Autumn (*H. Armstrong Roberts*)
5. Winter (*Philip D. Gendreau*)

CLASSIFIED INDEX

GENERAL CLASSIFICATIONS

ALPHABETICAL INDEX

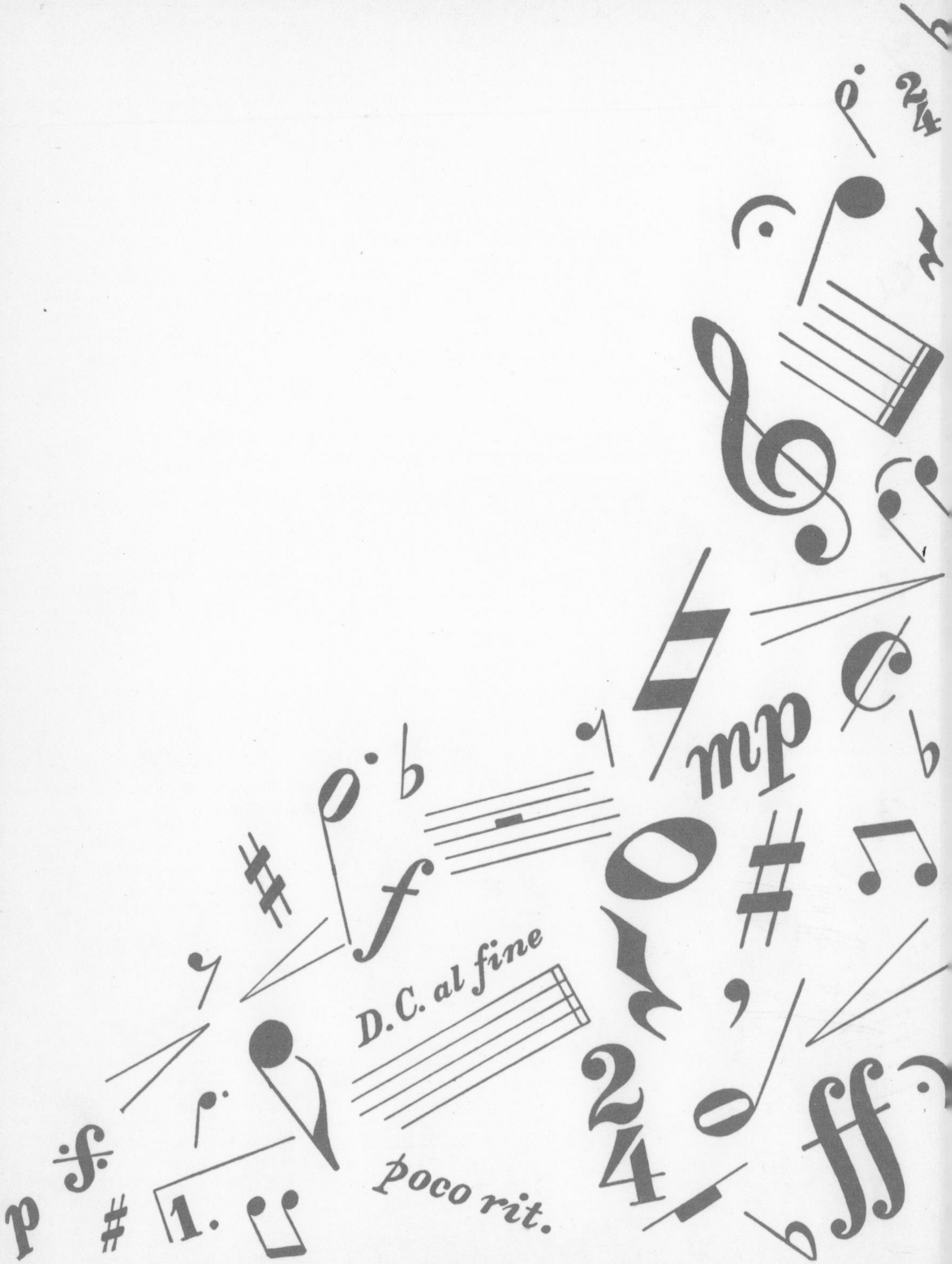
D.C. al fine
poco rit.